The
BEET SUGAR
Story

Third edition, completely revised, of the
book originally published as *The Silver Wedge*

PUBLISHED BY THE UNITED STATES BEET SUGAR ASSOCIATION

WASHINGTON, D.C.

1959

May 1959

Introduction

Each year in twenty-two states across more than half the nation a drama of farm and factory occurs.

It is the sugar beet harvest — one of the most concentrated movements of a perishable crop to market in America. In most of these states, the peak of the harvest is reached in October and some fifteen million tons of beets must be harvested before winter weather sets in. From dawn to dusk thousands of ingenious machines pull the beets from the earth, remove crown and spreading green leaves, and load the beet roots into waiting trucks. By truck and train the beets speed to the sugar factories. Here, for twenty-four hours out of every twenty-four — by processes mechanical and chemical — sparkling white, pure sugar is extracted from the beets.

Activity is at its peak during the harvest and sugar-making campaign. But all through the year the beneficial effect of the United States beet sugar industry is felt in the economy and security of the nation, and in the health and energy of its people.

Annually, the beet sugar industry pours some half billion dollars of new wealth into the nation's economy. The effects are direct in the twenty-two states where beets are grown — from the Great Lakes through the high plateaus of the Mountain States to the West Coast. Strengthened and diversified farm income and sugar factory payrolls stabilize family and community life, build schools and roads. In the rest of the nation the effects are felt through the purchases by sugar beet growers and factory workers of many products of American industry, from tractors to tricycles, and through purchases of supplies and services by the sugar companies. Few farm crops add so much income per acre to the revenue of America's transportation systems. Mines and quarries keep busy supplying coal, coke and limerock. On farm and in factory, the beet sugar industry makes good customers for American business.

The product of this industry has universal appeal for a simple and understandable reason: It tastes good. The sweetness of sugar enhances the flavor of other foods, and in itself sugar is delightful to eat.

Nutritionists, however, stress the importance of sugar as a food for another reason: the *energy* it provides.

For life itself cannot exist without foods that produce energy. They enable the heart to pump, they stimulate the cells of the brain. They make it possible to breathe, to work, to play, to talk.

And sugar is the most effective energy food — the purest, most readily available, most pleasant and cheapest of them all.

Sugar has other important uses — in the manufacture of medicines, for example, and various industrial products.

The science of sucrochemistry is opening far-reaching possibilities for a multitude of new sugar-based products.

But it is the importance of sugar as an energy food that has caused nations to seek ways of attaining a certain self-sufficiency in sugar supply. A tropical grass — sugar cane — produces sugar; but because of the nature of the plant itself cane does not grow satisfactorily in northern climates. Here in the temperate zone, where the greatest modern civilizations have developed and the greatest contributions to science and the arts have been made, sugar is indispensable to national welfare. Consequently it is here that nations, acting with foresight or repenting bitter experience, have consistently encouraged sugar production at home from a source other than cane, in volume sufficient to supply a part, if not all, of their requirements.

Thus it is that the sugar beet has become a vital and necessary part of the agricultural and industrial economy of the United States and other nations of the temperate zone.

The sugar beet itself is a most versatile and unusual plant. It withstands adverse weather better than most crops, and is adaptable to widely varying climates, altitudes and soils. In the United States the sugar beet thrives in such contrasting areas as the Imperial Valley of Southern California — where the altitude is below sea level — and the San Luis Valley of Colorado, which is 7,000 feet above sea level. It grows well in both acid and alkaline soils.

Under the activating force of energy from the sun, the beet manufactures sugar in its broad, green leaves, and stores the sugar in the root. Sugar itself is a combination of carbon, hydrogen and oxygen. Thus after sugar is extracted from the root, the vegetable matter of the plant remains for other uses. Beet pulp, beet tops, molasses and other syrups are ideal livestock feeds and are the foundation of extensive livestock feeding operations in beet-producing states.

The sugar taken from the sugar beet is pure sucrose — as is the sugar that comes from cane. All sucrose is identical, no matter what plant in nature it comes from.

The story of sugar, the sugar beet, and the industry that has been built around the beet in the United States is a fascinating and romantic narrative. Essentially this is a story of plant and man and machine combining to wrest energy from the sun in a particularly pleasing form, for the benefit of mankind.

TABLE OF

CONTENTS

SOLAR BATTERIES

Turned toward the sun, the Bell Solar Battery (*left*) captures the sun's energy and transforms it into electrical energy for operating telephone circuits. The spreading green leaves of the sugar beet (*above*) are truly a "solar battery" of nature — storing the energy of the sun in the form of sugar, for quick conversion by the human body to human energy.

Chapter One

THE MIRACLE OF
SUNSHINE, AIR AND WATER

The "Solar Battery" of Nature

One day in 1955, a farmer in southwest Georgia lifted his telephone receiver and switched on an electrical current generated by sunshine. He and his neighbors were the first persons whose telephone lines were powered by a scientific marvel called a solar battery, which converts the sun's energy directly into electrical energy. The heart of the device used in Georgia was an array of 432 silicon disks, each no larger than a quarter, which enabled the battery to capture and store enough solar energy in two days of sunshine to operate an entire community's rural telephone circuits for a full month.

Correctly hailed as a great achievement of this scientific age, solar batteries found even more spectacular uses by 1958. Built into American satellites or "artificial moons" circling the earth, such batteries converted sunshine to electricity for operating the radios that sent scientists a wealth of new information about outer space.

And yet there is really nothing new in the fact that man is using the energy that flows from the sun in a huge and constant stream. Man's use of solar energy is truly as ancient as human life itself. Since man first tasted root or fruit, he has used converted energy from the sun to walk, to run, to breathe — to sustain life itself.

The "solar battery" which from the beginning of time has captured the energy of the sun for mankind is not an array of silicon disks. It is the simple yet highly complex and truly miraculous green leaf of a growing plant. Here occurs the food-manufacturing process upon which all life on this planet depends. The prophet Isaiah wrote that "all flesh is grass," and in the final analysis it is true that all animate life, human and animal, depends upon plant life for food, fuel, clothing and shelter.

In the green leaf of a growing plant occurs the process that scientists call photosynthesis. It is a sugar-manufacturing process. The raw materials are water, air and sunshine. The process works like this:

The roots of a plant take up tremendous quantities of water from the soil, and the moisture moves up through the plant as if it were a wick, finally reaching the leaves. Through the pores (or *stomata*) in the leaves, carbon dioxide from the air enters the leaves. Thus the plant obtains the necessary ingredients for making sugar — hydrogen and oxygen from water, and carbon from the carbon dioxide in the air.

But to achieve the union (or synthesis) of these ingredients in order to form a new compound, the plant requires a supply of energy. This energy is found in sunlight. In the presence of light the union of carbon, hydrogen and oxygen takes place — and sugar is formed.

By means of this process all plants make sugar in some form; and by eating vegetables, fruits and grains man absorbs the energy thus provided and his body converts it into human energy. Some plants manufacture and store more sugar than others, and from some of these man has found it practicable to extract the sugar in crystallized form — "crystallized sunshine, air and water." Sugar is the most easily assimilated energy food — the food most readily and quickly converted by the body into human energy that enables man to live, breathe, perform his multitudinous tasks, and enjoy his pleasures. Sugar thus is truly solar energy, obtained from the sun for man's use by the "solar battery" of nature, the green leaf of a growing plant.

All Sucrose Is Identical

The sugar of commerce — the sugar with which you are most familiar — is technically *sucrose*. Just as pure gold can be extracted from various ores, so pure sugar (sucrose) can be extracted from various plants. In either case, the fully refined product is the pure substance — gold is gold and sugar is sugar — no matter what the source.

Pure sucrose can be taken from palm trees, maple trees, sor-

SUGAR CRYSTALS

The sugar of commerce is sucrose, and all sucrose is identical in chemical composition and architecture, no matter what its source in nature. Photo *above* shows greatly enlarged sugar crystals. There are millions of such crystals in the 14 teaspoons of pure sucrose extracted from the average two-pound sugar beet (*below*).

ghum, watermelons, and many other plants, just as it can from sugar beets and sugar cane. After exhaustive tests, the United States Department of Agriculture reported that "by no chemical test can the pure crystallized sugar from these different sources be distinguished." That pure beet and pure cane sugars are identical has been further confirmed extensively by other government chemists, by agricultural colleges, home economics teachers, dietitians, physicians, and notably by large manufacturers of canned goods, candy, bakery products, confections, jellies and preserves.

Millions of American housewives, verifying the scientific fact that all sucrose is identical, have learned from experience in their own kitchens that with today's modern refining methods there is no sweeter, purer, finer or whiter sugar than beet sugar — for every food use. They have learned that whenever difficulties are encountered in cooking, candy-making, jelly-making, etc., they are caused by factors other than the source of the sugar. Whether the sugar comes from the beet or cane has no bearing, for example, on the jelling of a fruit mixture. Fruit mixtures jell when pectin, acid and sugar are present in the proper proportions.

For generations, European cooking traditions have been based on beet sugar. The tastiest creations of French chefs and the finest English jams and biscuits call for its use. And since Europeans rely primarily on beet sugar, humorous situations have arisen when they have been forced to change to cane sugar. During World War I, for example, when England's normal supply of beet sugar from the continent was cut off, a chorus of protests arose from cooks and food processors. Dissatisfaction reached such a state that *The International Sugar Journal*, published in London, gave recognition to it in an article which said:

". . . There still exists among many manufacturers of jam, confectionery, biscuits, condensed milk, etc., a prejudice against cane sugar. . . . . . It is desirable that in the near future a thorough investigation should be made into the question, preferably by an official body. It should be established definitely and convincingly whether or not cane sugar can be used for all purposes for which beet sugar is suitable."

Sugar Chemistry

Although "sugar" to most of us means the sugar of commerce, which is sucrose, to the chemist the word "sugar" signifies more than a hundred substances. They differ in appearance and proper-

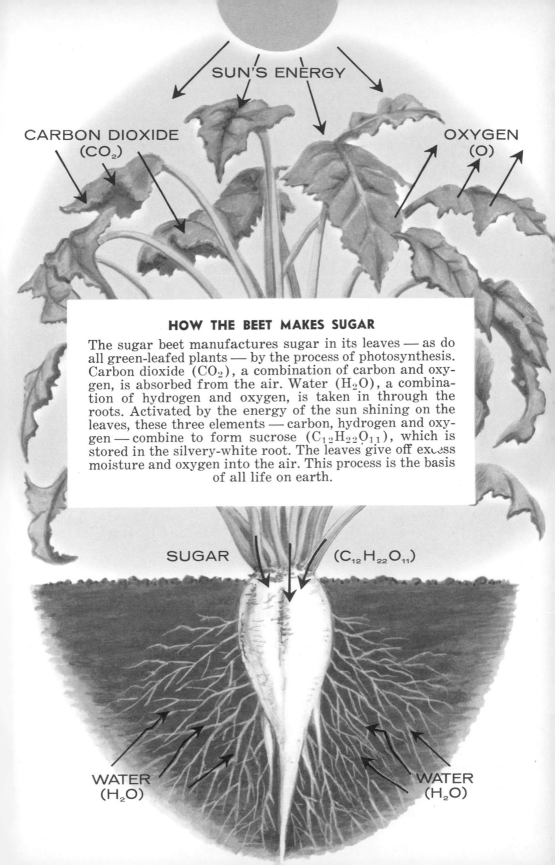

SUN'S ENERGY

CARBON DIOXIDE
(CO_2)

OXYGEN
(O)

HOW THE BEET MAKES SUGAR

The sugar beet manufactures sugar in its leaves — as do all green-leafed plants — by the process of photosynthesis. Carbon dioxide (CO_2), a combination of carbon and oxygen, is absorbed from the air. Water (H_2O), a combination of hydrogen and oxygen, is taken in through the roots. Activated by the energy of the sun shining on the leaves, these three elements — carbon, hydrogen and oxygen — combine to form sucrose ($C_{12}H_{22}O_{11}$), which is stored in the silvery-white root. The leaves give off excess moisture and oxygen into the air. This process is the basis of all life on earth.

SUGAR   ($C_{12}H_{22}O_{11}$)

WATER
(H_2O)

WATER
(H_2O)

ties, but all are composed of carbon, hydrogen and oxygen. The atoms of hydrogen and oxygen are nearly always associated in the ratio of two of hydrogen to one of oxygen — that is, in the ratio in which they are combined in water, the chemical formula for which is H_2O.

Chemists classify sugars according to the arrangement of atoms in the sugar molecule. The two main broad classifications are monosaccharides and disaccharides — although more complex sugars called trisaccharides and polysaccharides are also recognized. The chemical formula of the monosaccharides is $C_6H_{12}O_6$. Among the sugars in this group are glucose (sometimes called dextrose), which is found in corn, and fructose (also called levulose), found in certain fruits. The disaccharides are identified by the chemical formula, $C_{12}H_{22}O_{11}$ — which means that a molecule consists of twelve atoms of carbon, twenty-two atoms of hydrogen and eleven atoms of oxygen. The sugar we have been discussing — sucrose — is in this group, which also includes maltose (malt sugar) and lactose (milk sugar).

Thus have the chemists analyzed and put into precise chemical terms the relationship among the elements in a molecule of sugar.

But useful as they are to those who use sugar in food and other products, and for understanding sugar's role in human nutrition, the formulas in themselves cannot convey the importance of sugar to mankind.

For sugar is the physical basis of all life. It is the first substance manufactured by all green-leaved plants, which in turn support all human and animal life. Through sugar, energy of the sun is made available to man. Sugar truly is the miracle of sunshine, air and water.

Chapter Two

EARLY SUGAR HISTORY

The romantic story of sugar reaches far back into the shadowy mists of ancient times, and to view the American beet sugar industry in proper perspective it is best to take first a brief glimpse at the fascinating role sugar has played in the history of the world.

Early Sugar Cane History

Primitive man satisfied his hunger for sweets by eating honey and plants containing sugar. Sugar cane apparently was known in India and elsewhere in the Orient hundreds of years before the Christian era, and the Old Testament twice mentions it. In Jeremiah 6:20, the prophet asks, "To what purpose cometh there to me incense from Sheba, and the sweet cane from a far country?" In Isaiah 43:24, the accusation — "Thou hast bought me no sweet cane with money" — is evidence that even in Isaiah's time sugar cane was an article of commerce.

Europe discovered the art of crystallizing sugar in the fourth century, but refining in the modern sense can hardly be said to have been practiced until the fourteenth century. At first the sweet crystals were used largely for medicinal purposes, and not until the Elizabethan period did sugar become an article of household use.

Arabs became acquainted with sugar when they swept over Persia, and as they continued westward they extended the art of cane cultivation to the northern coast of Africa, and thence into Spain. Cane plantations were found by the Crusaders in Tripoli, Mesopotamia, Syria, Palestine, and Antioch, and they eventually became interested in the sugar trade, making Tyre the center of their operations. Once having acquired a taste for sugar, they were in no mood to discontinue its use when they returned to their

6

homes, and as a consequence a lively trade in sugar sprang up between northern Europe and the seaports of the Mediterranean.

Even before the Crusades, Venetian merchants had conducted a commerce in sugar, spices, silks and other products of the East. Ships were small, but the volume of trading was larger than might be imagined. In 1319, Tomaso Loredano, a Venetian merchant, sent a hundred thousand pounds of sugar to England to be exchanged for wool.

The passing years brought to Venice a virtual monopoly over the commerce in sugar, which her traders sought to protect and extend in every way possible. One such way offered itself in 1420 when an unnamed inventor perfected a method of refining. To gain control of the process, Venetians paid the inventor an amount equivalent to $120,000, which was ten times the cost of financing the first voyage of Columbus across the Atlantic. As the demand for sugar grew, the merchants of Venice increased prices, resulting in widespread complaint in Europe.

The Portuguese were the first to take effective action against the monopoly of the Venetians. In 1419 Prince Henry the Navigator discovered Madeira, and there the Portuguese planted cuttings of cane they had obtained from Sicily. The cane grew abundantly. When the Azores, Cape Verde Islands and Canary Islands were discovered, cane was planted there also. By 1472 cane was being cultivated on virtually all the islands along the African coast as far south as St. Thomas. Lisbon grew in power and wealth. Venice passed the peak of its glory and began to decline.

Columbus brought cane to the New World, and in a letter to Ferdinand and Isabella he expressed satisfaction at "the way a few small canes planted here have taken root." To the Spaniards, also, belongs the credit for having developed cane production on a commercial scale in the West Indies, first in San Domingo. Sugar plantations there began to prosper after a cheap supply of labor — slaves imported from Africa — became available. The success of the venture in San Domingo led to the cultivation of cane in the other islands of the West Indies and on the mainland of South America. In all these places it flourished — perhaps, indeed, it flourished too well, for it nourished the fester of slavery for more than 150 years.

Early Sugar Beet History

Cane had been grown in the tropical areas of the New World generations before sugar extracted from the beet root made its first appearance in Europe. That is not to say, of course, that ancestors of the present sugar beet were unknown in bygone days. On the contrary, some scholars believe sugar beets were eaten by the laborers who piled up the pyramid of Cheops, Egyptian Pharaoh who lived about three thousand years before Christ.

Apparently the beet grew in wild state in parts of Asia, and at an early time it was cultivated in southern Europe as well as in Egypt. Classical writers made many references to the beet root. Hippocrates, the Greek physician, said that a beet broth had a salutary effect in treating certain ailments, and that beet leaves dipped in wine had healing properties when applied to wounds.

Plautus, Cicero, Suetonius and Columella all have something to tell about the beet. At various times it was proposed that beet juice be used as a hair tonic, for cleaning the teeth and for restoring flavor of wine that had soured.

The literature of the Middle Ages contains allusions to the beet and its importance to the diet. Yet other qualities were not passed by unnoticed. The Portuguese poet, Gil Vicente, who lived about 1500, wrote a merry couplet which may be loosely translated:

> "One's head should have as much of brains
> As the sweetness which the beet contains."

Early in the 1600's an observant Frenchman, Olivier de Serres, wrote: "The beet root when boiled yields a juice similar to syrup of sugar." Another century passed before extraction of sugar from the beet was demonstrated to be practical on a commercial scale. Meantime repeated efforts, all unsuccessful, were made to obtain sugar from apples, pears, corn, quinces, mulberries, plums, figs, pumpkins, watermelons and even from walnuts and chestnuts.

Beet Sugar in Europe

Events which resulted in establishment of the beet sugar industry in Europe involved, in this order, the laboratory experiments of a German chemist, the perseverance of one of his students, the backing of a Prussian king, the urgent needs of an empire at war, and the dynamic action of a French emperor.

In 1747 Andreas Marggraf, a German chemist, proved in his laboratory that the beet root stored pure sucrose and that it could be extracted in crystalline form. But no one seemed excited — probably because the process of extraction had all the earmarks of a laboratory trick. Marggraf had sliced the beets, then dried and pulverized them. On eight ounces of the powder he poured six ounces of alcohol, and placed the mixture over a slow fire. When the liquid came to a boil, he withdrew it from the fire and filtered it into a flagon which he corked and allowed to stand for some weeks. At the end of the time, he reported, crystals had formed — crystals which had all the physical and chemical characteristics of sugar from cane.

The enthusiasm that might have been expected at the announcement of Marggraf's discovery was saved for another forty years until Franz Karl Achard, one of his pupils, planted beets on a rather extensive scale and succeeded in obtaining a substantial amount of sugar from them. He calculated that a good, low-grade sugar could be produced for six cents a pound, a figure which seemed so low that members of the French Institute investigated his claims. These learned gentlemen found that the extraction of sugar from beets on a commercial scale was wholly possible — but, they said, the cost probably would reach eighteen cents a pound.

Frederick William III, King of Prussia, interested himself in Achard's work and provided funds for the world's first beet sugar factory, which was erected at Cunern, Silesia. Operations were begun in 1802, and in relatively few years it became apparent that, with intelligent management, the project was bound to succeed. The French, meantime, had been corresponding with Achard, and sugar factories were hopefully built at Saint-Ouen and Chelles. But because the French lacked technical knowledge and practical experience, their enterprises miscarried, just as so many other beet sugar developments were to fail for the same reasons in later years. As a result of these disappointments, attention was diverted from beets to grapes, and French scientists tried to imprison crystals of grape sugar in their test-tubes. Their efforts were partly successful, and for a time grape syrup to some extent replaced cane syrup.

This determination to develop a supplementary source of sugar on the Continent of Europe was rooted in need. The French, embroiled in the Napoleonic Wars, found themselves cut off from the sugar which usually flowed to them from the West Indies, and prices mounted rapidly to more than a dollar a pound. It was a matter of national concern, just as our own sugar supplies have concerned us during periods of war.

The experiments with grapes were finally abandoned, and scientists turned back to the beet. One of them, M. Deyeaux, pharmacist to the Emperor, successfully produced a few loaves of "perfectly crystallized sugar, very white, very sweet — enjoying, in a word, all the properties of the best cane sugar." Another was Benjamin Delessert, who erected a small factory at Passy and went about his business without the fanfare attending the activities at Saint-Ouen and Chelles. By January, 1811, he had made a quantity of well-crystallized beet sugar.

The achievement was reported to the Minister of the Interior, who in turn relayed the news to Napoleon. It needs the enthusiasm of a French writer to describe how Napoleon reacted: "Enraptured, Napoleon cried out, 'We must see this. Let us go at once.' After having seen the results for himself, the Emperor approached Delessert, and, taking off the Cross of Honor which he wore on his breast, he pinned it on Delessert. Next day the *Moniteur* announced that a great revolution in French commerce had been wrought."

On March 18, 1811, he ordered his Minister of the Interior to take "all steps" to encourage the growing of sugar beets and the erection of beet sugar factories. Significantly, he requested the Minister to advise French farmers "that the growing of beet root improves the soil, and that the residue of the fabrication furnishes an excellent food for cattle."

Seven days later Napoleon "took steps" himself, and by the stroke of a quill pen brought a new industry into being. At the Palace of the Tuileries he signed a decree that 79,000 acres of land be planted to beets as quickly as possible, and that six experimental stations be established for the instruction of farmers and landowners. Moreover, he appropriated one million francs to implement the program.

Political cartoonists of the period found in Napoleon's interest in the sugar beet a topic suited to their wit. One contemporary cartoon shows the Emperor squeezing the juice of a beet into his coffee. His son, the infant King of Rome, sits in a nearby cradle with a beet pressed to his mouth, while an acid-faced nurse tells the child: "Suce, mon cheri, suce! Ton père dit que c'est du sucre" — "Suck, dear, suck! Your father says it is sugar."

And sugar it was! — sugar that energized Napoleon's armies! The dire need for a quick-energy food gave the beet sugar industry its first big commercial push. As a result of Napoleon's various decrees 334 small beet sugar factories were erected in France in 1812 and 1813.

But the industry born of urgent necessity was shortly to experience extreme difficulties. Waterloo — June 18, 1815 —

NAPOLEON AND BEET SUGAR

A French artist of the time envisioned this as the scene when the Minister
of the Interior presented Napoleon I with loaves of beet sugar "made in
France." The exhibit and the dire need of Napoleon's armies for the quick
energy that only sugar can give impelled the Emperor to decree widespread
planting of sugar beets and erection of beet processing plants in France.
Thus the extraction of sugar from sugar beets, first developed by German
chemists, became a full-fledged industry by decree of a French emperor.

crushed an industry as well as an Emperor. With the downfall of
Napoleon, the blockade was lifted and ships from the West Indies
hastened to dump their cargoes of accumulated sugar into the
ports of the Continent. Prices collapsed. The newly established
beet sugar factories were hit hard by the war's aftermath. Strug-
gling with primitive processing methods and raw materials of
low quality, the homeland industry was unable to withstand the
effects of this wholesale dumping of cane sugar produced by slave
labor in the French Colonies. One year after Waterloo, only a
single beet sugar mill, at Arras, remained in operation in France.

Yet even in these desperate straits the industry had champions who refused to become despondent. A few brief years had
taught them that the beet had a definite and valuable place in agriculture. Bit by bit, improvements in the processes of manufacture more than doubled the percentage of sugar extracted from a
ton of beets — although it still was low by modern standards.
Better beets — richer in sugar — were developed. These improvements, and the passage of laws which sought to equalize the conditions of competition between the producers of the Indies and
those at home, gradually brought about a restoration of the industry in France. Louis Philippe, French ruler from 1830 to 1848,
and Napoleon III, who reigned from 1852 to 1870, especially recognized the value of a home-produced sugar supply, and initiated
effective government programs to encourage the beet sugar industry.

Meanwhile, the industry was becoming established in other
European countries, notably Germany. A German sugar school,
set up in January, 1812, drew students from all parts of continental Europe and they in turn had a profound influence in the
later development of the industry throughout Europe. If the
growth of the industry in Germany was slower than in France,
it was nevertheless founded on a more substantial basis, possibly
because the Germans were not torn by conflicting loyalties between overseas production and homeland production. The German
industry, however, like that of France, suffered a severe setback
by the flood of slave-produced sugar from the tropics which followed the downfall of Napoleon and the lifting of the European
blockade. But as in France, persistent efforts and governmental
encouragement re-established the industry.

In any event, the emancipation of slaves in the West Indies
finally put the European beet sugar industry in a position in
which it was able to offer more effective competition to tropical
sugars. By 1854 the industry was operating on a large scale over

most of the continent, and soon thereafter European-produced beet sugar was being exported in sizeable quantities. Today, beet sugar is produced from the United Kingdom to Russia, from Finland to Italy — in every European country but Norway and Portugal. And sugar beet culture has spread to much of the rest of the world: to the Near East — Turkey, Syria, Afghanistan, Iran; to the Far East — Japan, Manchuria; to the Americas — the United States, Canada, Chile; and to other places. The importance of the beet sugar industry to the economies of several nations is recognized by national programs of encouragement and protection.

Chapter Three

THE SUGAR BEET
TAKES ROOT IN AMERICA

For many years a variety of wild sugar beet has been observed growing in central California. This fact, coupled with statements in an eighteenth century manuscript of a Spanish explorer, has led to conjecture that California Indians may have developed a method of extracting sugar from the beet before Europeans did. Pedro Fages, a Spanish captain who explored parts of California between 1768 and 1772, wrote in 1775: "Those [the tribes] of the Sierras made also quantities of molasses, candy, and sugar, that is not unworthy of the fame of these people, and it is extracted from certain species of vegetables. . ."

Be that as it may, the first attempts by the white man to establish a beet sugar industry in America occurred near the East Coast rather than the West, and the industry's pioneers turned to Europe for information and for seed.

Fifty Years of Pioneering

Men of vision in the New World watched with intense interest the rebirth of the beet sugar industry in France and its development elsewhere in Europe. They saw a three-fold advantage to be gained through beet sugar production in the United States: freedom from almost complete dependence on foreign countries for sugar; benefits a new industry would bring to the young nation's economy; and the improvement in agricultural practices which beet culture would encourage. If the technical skill of the early American champions of beet sugar had matched their vision and enthusiasm, the industry would have become a permanent part of the American scene in the first half of the nineteenth century. As it was, nearly fifty years elapsed between the first known attempt

14

and lasting success at establishing beet sugar manufacture in the United States.

The first effort of which any comprehensive record remains was launched in 1830 by James Ronaldson of Philadelphia, first president of the Franklin Institute of that city. He interested some friends in the project, and together they organized the Beet Sugar Society of Philadelphia. In 1836 the Society sent James Pedder to Europe to make a thorough study. He shipped back six hundred pounds of beet seed, which unfortunately was planted too late in the season to produce beets good for anything but cattle feed. Mr. Pedder's glowing report of the possibilities for a beet sugar industry in the United States remains today as the principal accomplishment of the Beet Sugar Society of Philadelphia.

The next two attempts resulted in something more substantial than a report — the erection of two sugar factories.

At Northampton, Massachusetts, Edward Church and David Lee Child, who had observed beet sugar production in France, sparked the effort which produced the first beet sugar in the United States, some 1,300 pounds, in 1838. But economic difficulties beset this venture, and the factory closed its doors forever in 1841.

Meanwhile, many miles to the west, at White Pigeon, Michigan, farmers and townsfolk organized the Beet Sugar Company in 1837 and built a factory in 1838. Despite a $5,000 loan from the State of Michigan, this venture also failed — largely because of lack of technical knowledge and skill.

More than a decade passed before the logic behind the production of sugar in the temperate zone of the continental United States reasserted itself through action, this time in one of the most colorful episodes of sugar history.

In 1847 the members of a new religious movement, the Mormon Church, settled in Utah and sought to create, so far as possible, a self-sufficient community. Cut off by time and distance from the eastern states, the Mormons were forced to pay dearly for all articles they could not produce themselves. One dollar a pound was the usual price for sugar.

Thus it was with a practical zeal that John Taylor studied the beet sugar industry in France while he served there as a missionary for the Church. With Church approval, he organized the Deseret Manufacturing Company with the express purpose of establishing the industry in Utah. At a cost of $12,500, the company purchased a complete sugar manufacturing outfit, which arrived in New Orleans from France in April, 1852. The heavy

machinery was floated up the Mississippi and Missouri Rivers by
boat to Fort Leavenworth, Kansas, where it was loaded into covered wagons drawn by fifty-two ox teams. From Kansas to Utah
was a slow and painful journey in those days. Wagons broke
down; oxen strayed; food supplies ran low. It was not until No-
vember that the party convoying the equipment arrived, hungry
and cold, at its destination.

It would be pleasant to record that, after such hardships, the
attempt of courageous pioneers to produce sugar in Utah was an
immediate success. On the contrary, it was a distinct failure, because, as so often before and after, the promoters lacked technical information to temper their enthusiasm. The factory produced
only an inedible syrup.

Even before the Mormon venture the possibility of producing
sugar in the West had been investigated. A petition filed January
8, 1841, by Guadalupe Miranda and Carlos Beaubien asked that
a portion of land, now included within Colorado, be granted by the
governor of the province of New Mexico for the culture of sugar
beets.

Colorado apparently was interested in sugar during the ex-
citing period of the Gold Rush, for as early as 1865 Peter Magnes,
a Swedish immigrant, prophesied: "If we had beet sugar factories
in Colorado, I imagine Colorado farmers would produce more gold
than all the mines in the mountains." His prophecy has been ful-
filled over and over, but Colorado was to wait until the turn of
the century to see her first sugar factory in operation.

In other states, interest ran high and then ebbed as failure
overtook all fourteen sugar factories erected between 1838 and
1879 — in Maine, Massachusetts, Delaware, Michigan, Illinois,
Wisconsin, Utah and California. But the American pioneering
spirit is tough, and disappointment in one area seemed to spur
hope and enthusiasm in another. Perseverance finally won.

Success in California, 1879

To E. H. Dyer goes the credit for establishing the beet sugar
industry in the United States on a successful basis, in 1879, at
Alvarado, California. The factory at Alvarado, near the east shore
of San Francisco Bay, was first built in 1870, but the original
company went bankrupt and the machinery was moved out. With
a group of associates, Mr. Dyer took over the buildings in 1879,
installed different equipment, and put the operation on a paying
basis. This was the first solid demonstration in the United States

that sugar could be extracted from beets successfully and profitably. After undergoing several renovations and enlargements, this historic factory was completely rebuilt in 1936 and is still in operation.

In 1888 at Watsonville, California, Claus Spreckels built the second successfully-operated beet sugar factory which, in that year, produced 1,000 tons of beet sugar.

The successes in California renewed interest in the beet sugar industry in other states. Henry Oxnard and his three brothers were among the first to take action. They went to Europe, made a careful study of the industry there, and in 1890 built a factory at Grand Island, Nebraska. In 1891 they built two more, one at Norfolk, Nebraska, and one at Chino, California. In the same year a factory was constructed by another group at Lehi, Utah, the first of its kind in the Intermountain area.

Other persons were prominent in this era of transition from pioneering setbacks to genuine success for the United States beet sugar industry.

One was Dr. Lewis S. Ware, a wealthy engineer and chemist, who spent large amounts of his own money distributing beet seed and literature in efforts to convince farmers and businessmen that the sugar beet was a desirable crop and that beet processing could be a sound business venture. Among the people he convinced were Mr. Dyer and Mr. Spreckels, whose successful factories justified Dr. Ware's confidence.

Another important influence during this period was Dr. Harvey W. Wiley, who won fame also as a sponsor of the Food and Drug Act. Chief chemist of the United States Department of Agriculture from 1874 to 1913, Dr. Wiley was officially as well as personally a sugar beet enthusiast. He distributed seeds to farmers and after making 8,000 analyses of beets grown in almost all the states of the Union, published an uncannily accurate map designating the most favorable areas for sugar beet growing in the United States. Later development of the industry has been almost entirely within the areas he indicated.

A third influential figure was James ("Tama Jim") Wilson, noted Secretary of Agriculture under Presidents McKinley, Theodore Roosevelt, and Taft. A firm believer in the importance of the sugar beet to the nation's future agriculture, Mr. Wilson was unremitting in his efforts to enlist capital for building new factories — so farmers could have a market for their beets. Seventy of the seventy-nine factories existing in 1915 were built during his tenure of office.

This official recognition and assistance of the Department of Agriculture were important to the continued progress of the newly-proven industry, but the governmental encouragement was also justified by the spread of the industry to other states after the successes in California and Nebraska. By 1900 thirty completely equipped beet sugar factories were operating successfully in eleven states from New York to the West Coast. It was evident at the turn of the century that the sugar beet had become at last firmly rooted in the economic as well as the agricultural soil of the United States. The industry was indeed national in scope.

The Industry Today

From those pioneering efforts and initial successes has emerged the American beet sugar industry of today. An integral part of the economy of twenty-two states, the industry exerts a beneficial influence that is felt throughout the nation.

For many thousands of farm families the sugar beet provides a major source of income and purchasing power, as well as a key to sound farm operations. More than three-score modern beet sugar processing plants — a far cry from the first crude factories at Northampton and White Pigeon — pour forth a stream of sparkling white, pure beet sugar that annually meets nearly one-fourth of the nation's sugar requirements.

A quick look at the extent of the industry that grew from those faltering beginnings may be obtained from the map on the opposite page. Further details will be found in tables in the Appendix, beginning on Page 78.

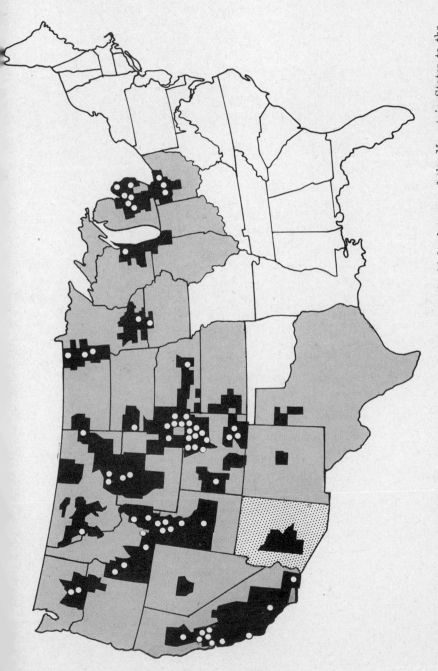

Twenty-two states — extending from the Great Lakes through the high plateaus of the Mountain States to the West Coast — produce sugar beets. More than three score beet sugar factories (indicated by white dots) are located in fifteen of those states. Beet-producing counties are indicated by black areas. A twenty-third state, Arizona, does not produce sugar beets for sugar, but is one of the major beet seed producing states.

19

Chapter Four

THE SUGAR BEET
IN AMERICAN AGRICULTURE

The Beet Means More Than Sugar

About the time the Mormons were making their first strenuous attempt to establish the beet sugar industry in Utah, a significant episode occurred in France. It helped to explain why foresighted Americans of that day believed the sugar beet could contribute importantly toward developing a well-rounded agriculture in this country. And it illustrated a fact that many American farmers later learned — that sugar beet culture brings benefits to agriculture extending far beyond the production of sugar itself.

In 1853, when Napoleon III, and his bride, Eugenie, were touring France, the peasants of Valenciennes built a triumphal arch to welcome them and to honor the two Napoleons who fostered the beet sugar industry. Across the top of the arch appeared the legend, "Sugar Manufacture," and under it, the likeness of Napoleon I, "Who Created It," and Napoleon III, "Who Protected It."

Under the portrait of the first Napoleon was the inscription:
"Before the manufacture of beet sugar the *arrondissement* of Valenciennes produced 695,750 bushels of wheat and fattened 700 oxen."

And under the image of Napoleon III, the "protector," the words were:
"Since introduction of the manufacture of beet sugar the *arrondissement* of Valenciennes produces 1,157,750 bushels of wheat and fattens 11,500 oxen."

Here was an increase, credited to the sugar beet, of 66 per cent in wheat production, and a gain of more than 1,500 per cent

THE SUGAR BEET ROOT

This picture illustrates one reason why the sugar beet is ideal for planting in rotation with shallow-rooted crops. The tap root of the sugar beet extends as much as six to seven feet deep, and smaller roots reach out in all directions, aerating the soil and drawing nutrients from levels not required by other crops. When the beet is pulled from the ground at harvest, the lower part of the tap root and the tiny rootlets remain, decaying and adding fertility and humus to the soil. Notice that beet roots extend more than twice the depth of the yardstick next to second beet from left.

in livestock fattening. If it seems curious that the amount of sugar produced was not mentioned, the omission merely emphasizes the attitude held by some Europeans that sugar is a by-product rather than a primary product of beet culture. While this attitude may unduly minimize the value of the sugar obtained from the beet, it does accentuate the striking effect of the sugar beet on the agriculture of the areas where it is grown.

For unlike many other crops the sugar beet serves more than one purpose. It has earned its eminent position in American agriculture for three primary reasons:

(1) It promotes soil fertility and sound farming practices. The sugar beet requires and therefore brings about a progressive system of diversified farming. Yields of other crops traditionally improve following beet production.

(2) By-products of the sugar beet provide an important feed for beef cattle, sheep, and dairy herds. In many areas the beet thus promotes a sound crop-and-livestock farm operation.

(3) Because of the sugar it produces, the beet is an important and dependable cash crop. For many farm families, the sugar beet is the most reliable source of income, year after year.

The Sugar Beet in Crop Rotation

One reason for the sugar beet's unique position in agriculture is its importance in a sound crop rotation. Good farming practice requires a variation in crops. Continuous planting of the same land to the same crop year after year almost inevitably results in agricultural and economic troubles. At least one of the crops in a good rotation should be an intensively cultivated row crop — such as sugar beets, corn, potatoes, cotton, beans, tobacco and garden vegetables.

Successful production of these crops requires a loosening of the earth around the plants at intervals during growth. This action breaks up crust and clods, improves the physical condition of the soil. It destroys weeds while they are still young and prevents their reseeding and dispersion. Sugar beets require cultivation not only between the rows but also between the plants in the row. Introduction of sugar beets has been a principal factor in controlling weeds in many farming areas. On the other hand, with continuous planting to hay, grain or other crops which are not ordinarily cultivated after planting, the land gradually becomes infested with soil pests, weeds and other foreign growth, and subject to inroads of plant diseases and insect pests.

Rotation is essential for many reasons other than the benefits of cultivation. In fact, cultivated crops themselves often are alternated, such as tomatoes, beans and other row crops in some areas. Plants feed at different depths in the soil. A plant with shallow roots, such as beans, tends to exhaust soil nutrients near the surface and should be alternated with a "deep-feeder" having long roots that tend to obtain more of their nutrients at deeper levels in later stages of growth. Moreover, different plants, even if feeding at the same level, may require varying proportions of a given soil element; rotating crops helps to prevent exhausting all the available supply of a single element. Rotation thus promotes soil equilibrium. Decaying residues of previous crops increase the amount of organic matter in the soil and benefit crops to follow. Pests which harm one crop may not affect another — may, in fact, die out when another crop is grown in the soil.

Proper rotation is essential, yet climate and soil impose limitations. Few crops grow well in all latitudes or in all soil types. Sugar beets grow successfully in areas where conditions rule out certain other crops. Beets thrive throughout the northern latitudes of the United States, in Canada, and as far south as the Mexican border, at elevations varying from below sea level to an altitude of 7,000 feet, and in a wide variety of soils. The crop exhibits a unique tolerance to alkali, which is present in large areas of land in arid regions of western states. Extensive development of such lands has been materially helped in many instances by the introduction of sugar beet culture.

The form and nature of the beet itself help explain why general farm conditions improve where sugar beets are grown. The root system penetrates the ground to as much as six or seven feet, a mechanical disturbance beneficial in itself. When the beet is pulled at harvest time, the greater part of the feeder-root system remains in the ground. Decomposing, it contributes to fertility. Beet tops, removed from the rest of the plant during the harvesting process, sometimes are plowed under, thus serving as "green manure" and adding further to the soil's fertility.

The increased yield of other crops in the beet rotation depends, of course, on many factors — such as management skill, type of soil, climate, irrigation and rainfall. Nevertheless, it has been conservatively estimated that a 15 per cent increase in the yield of wheat and a 10 per cent increase in yields of some other

THE VERSATILE SUGAR BEET

The sugar beet thrives in the high plateaus of the Rocky Mountain states (*above*) at altitudes as high as 7,000 feet above sea level — such as in the San Luis Valley of Colorado — and it grows equally well even below sea level. The photo *below* shows a beet sugar factory in the heart of the producing region of the Imperial Valley of southern California. The line high on the sugar storage bin marks sea level.

crops may be expected when the beet is introduced into the cycle of rotation. Other instances have been reported of 75 per cent higher yields of some other crops following the introduction of beet culture to the land.

By-Products for Livestock Feed

The sugar beet is literally two crops in one. Its principal product, sugar, is a vital energy food for human beings. Sugar beet by-products — tops, pulp and molasses — are highly nutritious feeds for livestock, and thus provide additional food and fiber for human beings as meat, milk and wool. (By-products that have non-agricultural uses will be discussed in Chapter Six.)

Years of experience in many parts of the country have shown that sugar beet by-products, fed with grain and alfalfa hay, will produce beef and mutton or lamb at lower cost than any other ration available in the United States, not even excepting the grain and alfalfa combinations fed in the corn-belt.

Sugar beet tops — the green leaves and a section of the "crown," or upper part of the beet — contain nearly 10 per cent digestible protein (on a dry matter basis) and show a marked Vitamin A effect when fed green or siloed green. Tests conducted over a fourteen-year period at a University of Nebraska experiment station showed sugar beet tops, pound for pound, equal to corn silage. "Pound for pound they are as good a source of feed roughage as alfalfa hay," the University of California found after exhaustive tests. In his book, *Beets and Meat,* E. J. Maynard points out that tops are also a fattening feed and that "each pound of well cured, dried tops is approximately equal to, or will replace, about one-half pound of grain."

In some areas, cured tops are baled and sold to commercial feeders if the beet farmer or his neighbors do not have feeding operations. Cured tops are also stacked and fed like hay. The fullest feed value of the tops is retained when they are siloed as soon as possible after removal from the beet. Many farmers have machinery that elevates the fresh, clean tops to trucks as part of the beet harvesting operation, for immediate hauling to silos. An acre producing twenty tons of beet roots for sugar will generally yield twelve to fifteen tons of green tops.

Beet pulp is the vegetable portion of the beet that remains after the sugar is removed in the processing plant. No less than beet tops, beet pulp is sought by dairymen and cattle and sheep feeders for their livestock. Sugar beet pulp contains carbohy-

SUGAR BEET TOPS FOR SILAGE

Tests by university agricultural scientists show that as feed for livestock, sugar beet top silage is equal to corn silage, pound for pound. Machines have been developed (*above*) for harvesting the beet tops like a separate crop, chopping and loading them into a truck. In the farmyard, beet tops may be blown into silos or conveyed as shown *below*.

NUTRITIOUS FEED FOR LIVESTOCK

The cattle on the other side of the fence in the photo *above* seem to be eagerly awaiting the sugar beet harvest so they can eat the succulent green tops. An equally desired feed for cattle and sheep is dried beet pulp, shown *below*. (Pencil indicates size of particles and pellets.) Through feeding these by-products, many sugar beet growers add to their income and build a diversified and balanced crop-and-livestock operation.

drates and also signficant quantities of protein and minerals. At some factories, pulp is stored in wet form and sold to farmers as they need it in their feeding operations. More commonly, however, most of the moisture is removed through mechanical pressure and evaporation, and the pulp is sold in dried form. Dried pulp is a concentrated livestock feed. Beet molasses is often added before the evaporation step, producing "molasses-dried" beet pulp. When the molasses is not added, the finished product is known as "plain dried" beet pulp. Dried pulp is also compressed into pellets for easier handling of the bulky material.

Another variation is ammoniated beet pulp. Cattle feeding tests at Oregon State College have shown it to be high protein feed giving results equal to or better than cottonseed meal.

Dried pulp is widely used as a basis for mixed feeds. It is used in the dairy, in the feed lot, and often as a supplemental feed on the range. Feeding experiments at state agricultural colleges have shown that "molasses-dried" beet pulp approximates the feeding value of corn, with certain additional benefits corn does not possess. A higher rate of animal survival results from the addition of sugar beet pulp to the ration, for in its specific effect on the animal, particularly the dairy cow, dried beet pulp goes beyond the properties of corn. To maintain high milk production, there is often a tendency to feed too heavy a grain component, which may cause death losses. But with dried pulp, which is bulky, fluffy, palatable, nutritious and highly absorptive, both the productivity and reproductivity of the dairy herd can be held at the most efficient level. Dried beet pulp increases the digestibility of other feeds in the ration.

Beet molasses is also a by-product of the sugar-extracting process. Although much molasses is mixed with pulp before the final drying, some molasses is also sold separately for mixing with other feeds. It may be added to practically any ration. Molasses gives the entire ration such an increased "taste appeal" that it has a replacement value equivalent to grain when the molasses is used in proper quantities. Manufacturers of mixed feeds recognize this desirable quality and often use molasses in their products.

The use of the sugar beet's by-products as livestock feed is another reason why the beet promotes better farming practices and builds a sounder agriculture. Beet tops, beet pulp in its various forms, and beet molasses have built an extensive sheep and cattle feeding industry in areas where corn and other feed crops have been relatively expensive. Through animals, nutrients taken from the soil by growing crops are restored to the land as manure,

MEAT FROM SUGAR BEET BY-PRODUCTS

Sugar beet by-products — tops, pulp and molasses — provide the basis for a large livestock feeding industry in many western states. Symbolizing the direct link of sugar beets and livestock is the photo *above* — showing cattle feeding on dried beet pulp in the foreground and a beet sugar factory in the background. *Below* are lambs fattened on sugar beet by-products.

and soil fertility is maintained. The by-products of the sugar beet therefore contribute to the stability of farms, towns and states.

An acre of land yielding twenty tons of beets will produce approximately 6,000 pounds of pure granulated sugar, and the by-products of the same acre, when included in a ration fed to live-stock, will produce from 400 to 600 pounds of meat or 5,000 to 6,000 pounds of milk. When by-products are fed on the farm that produced the beets, most of the vegetable part of the beet is returned to the soil through manure.

Refined sugar contains only carbon, hydrogen and oxygen. Thus millions of bags of sugar can be shipped out of beet-producing areas, yet leave behind the "big three" soil elements — nitrogen, phosphorus and potash — for return to the land. The sugar beet, therefore, is one of the most efficient crops known. No other crop grown in the temperate zone produces per acre so much food for man and feed for livestock as the sugar beet.

The Sugar Beet Is a Vital Cash Crop

To the farmer, cash income is a primary consideration in determining how he will invest his time and capital, and what he will produce from his labors. A compelling reason for growing sugar beets is that the beet is a dependable and highly valuable cash crop. The farmer contracts for the sale of his beets before he plants them; he has an assured market for his crop even before the seed is in the ground. Income from sugar beets, therefore, is something the farmer can count on, year in and year out, as a basis for the financial planning of his operations. The banker looks with favor upon the farmer who grows beets.

The early-day farmers needed a dependable cash crop that also had other attributes. Transportation to the populous markets for the products of the land was difficult and costly from this then remote country. In the sugar beet they found a cash crop and an answer to this perplexing problem. A ton of sugar beets went to distant markets as a few hundred pounds of sugar — taking little room in the box car and not piling up shipping charges that ate up the profits. Meat produced from beet by-products also served the need for a concentrated food to ship. Moreover, as the 200-foot smoke stacks of the sugar factories began to rise from the plains, another great need of the West was being met — manufacturing payrolls to supplement the income of the farmers and bring economic stability to the communities.

First through private initiative and later through reclamation programs of the government, irrigation projects brought water and life to the dry acres of the West. But a dependable cash crop was needed to form a basis for the financial success of the projects, as well as the financial success of the individual irrigation farmers. Sugar beets again provided the answer. Beets paid the water bills and lifted the mortgages. The Federal Reclamation Bureau consistently includes sugar beets as one of the recommended crops in new projects. Referring to the sugar beet industry as "the backbone of those federal reclamation projects where the crop is grown," a noted Commissioner of Reclamation, Elwood Mead, extolled the virtues of the sugar beet in words that still hold true today:

"It is one crop that contributes more than anything else to a rounded-out, complete agricultural program, gives winter and summer employment, enables the farmer to make the largest and best use of the surrounding grazing land, largest and best use of the alfalfa that is grown, and gives in an unusual measure a continuous employment for the family on the farms, with more stable income than anything else."

From Europe has come the statement that "if the sugar beet did not exist it would have to be invented." No one has yet invented — or discovered — another crop to equal the beet as a vital and dependable cash crop for vast regions of this nation, or as a crop that contributes so much to a well-rounded agriculture with benefits spreading to the entire nation.

Chapter Five

THE REVOLUTION IN BEET FARMING

All American agriculture has undergone a great mechanical revolution in the last third of a century, and the sugar beet farmer's method of producing his crop provides an example of the effects of this change. Ingenious machines have greatly reduced the amount of hand labor formerly required in beet production — just as the grain combine has replaced the laborious tasks of shocking the sheaves and loading the bundle wagon, so common in the wheat field a comparatively few years ago. Developments now in the laboratory, experiment station and machine shop promise still further changes.

Mechanization of sugar beet production plus improvement of beet seed strains and the application of more advanced farming methods have combined to raise the efficiency of American sugar beet farmers to new levels. According to officials of the United States Department of Agriculture, nowhere in the world are sugar beets produced with fewer man-hours per ton than in the United States. In fact, no foreign country produces any sugar crop — beet or cane — with fewer man-hours of field work per ton of sugar than are now required in the average American sugar beet field.

Harvest Now Completely Mechanized

The harvest was among the first of the major sugar beet field operations to be taken over by the machine. Adoption of mechanical harvesting came swiftly after practical machines were developed. The first began to appear in numbers soon after World War II, and in less than ten years the sugar beet harvest in America was virtually 100 per cent mechanized.

The harvest involved several distinct operations, and it was no simple task to develop a machine capable of performing them all. The traditional harvest was handled like this: A horse- or tractor-drawn "beet lifter" loosened the beets, then laborers pulled them, sliced off the crown and leaves with a broad-bladed beet knife, and heaped the beets in a pile for scooping into a wagon or truck. Despite the complicated nature of the beet harvest, several machines have been devised which perform all the operations in a single trip down the beet row — and, in addition, load the topped beets into trucks for hauling to the sugar factory.

To conserve the rich, green tops for livestock feed, some machines harvest the beet leaves separately, chopping and loading them into trucks for hauling to silos. Another kind of machine beats off the leaves with rubber flails, pulverizing the leaves for quicker disintegration when plowed under as "green manure." Another "scalps" the crown, leaving only the main part of the sugar-filled root in the ground for pulling and loading by another machine. Mechanical harvesters in most common use, however, perform all the operations in one trip through the field — pulling, topping and loading.

Implement manufacturers, scientists and management of the beet sugar processing companies, scientists of state agricultural colleges and the federal government, and the beet growers themselves have all cooperated to develop the variety of mechanical equipment now seen in American sugar beet fields at harvest time. For example, two of the first successful harvesters were developed — one in a small machine shop, the other by a major manufacturer — from basic ideas conceived by two beet growers, one in California and one in Colorado, working at the same time but independently of each other. To perfect the two machines, other growers and sugar company experts cooperated in field trials.

Some of the various types of harvesters in general use are shown in the accompanying illustrations.

Hand Blocking and Thinning Are on the Way Out

Similar cooperation has resulted in widespread mechanization of other phases of sugar beet production. Operations common to most crops — plowing, land leveling, disking, planting, etc. — have long been done mechanically by sugar beet farmers. But certain growing-season operations peculiar to beet production — blocking, thinning and cultivating between plants — are tasks that posed particularly difficult problems to the inventors of machines.

In mechanizing these operations, the work of agricultural engineers has been complemented, particularly in recent years, by

MECHANICAL SUGAR BEET HARVESTERS

Farm implement companies today manufacture many types of sugar beet harvesters. One kind, a refinement of the first beet harvester developed, features huge spiked wheels (*above*). As the machine moves down the rows of beets, plow blades under the wheels loosen the beets, which then are impaled on the spikes and lifted from the ground. Leafy tops are sliced off automatically before the beets are loaded into a truck. Examples of other kinds of harvesters are shown *below* and on the next page.

MACHINES IN SUGAR BEET FIELDS

American sugar beet farmers speedily adopted efficient mechanical methods of harvesting the crop as soon as satisfactory machines were developed. Often neighboring farmers assist one another with the harvest, and two mechanical harvesters in a single field are a common sight (*above*). Another kind of beet harvester is shown *below*. Although they differ mechanically, all harvesters have one thing in common: they have greatly increased the efficiency of the American sugar beet grower.

the research of plant scientists — because the basic problem was the beet seed itself. Blossoms on the normal sugar beet plant grow in clusters, and each cluster of flowers produces a group of seeds held together as a hard, tight ball covered with corklike material. When a seed ball is planted, therefore, two, three, four or more seedlings emerge, all close together and often intertwined.

Since the beets require "elbow room" for proper growth, they should be thinned to a point at which the plants stand at proper intervals in the row — six to twelve inches apart, depending upon soil and climatic conditions. In the traditional method of blocking and thinning, workers went through the field of solidly planted rows with short-handled hoes, first removing solid blocks of seedlings and then removing by finger work all but one plant from each blocked bunch.

This work must necessarily be done when the plants are small, about a month after planting, when four true leaves have appeared on each plant. Because the plants from a normal seed ball sprouted so closely together, a thinning machine could not be devised which would eliminate most of the plants and leave spaced single plants standing. The initial effort, therefore, had to be toward developing a beet seed ball which would produce only a single shoot.

The first substantial progress on this score was made in the early 1940's by scientists at the University of California, working under a grant provided by beet sugar companies. The researchers developed a method of reducing, by mechanical means, the number of seed germs in a seed ball and of mechanically sizing the reduced segments to uniform dimensions. This process was a tremendous advance. After various planting trials, the new "segmented" seed became the accepted seed for all sugar beet planting in the United States. This development alone has reduced the hand labor requirement by as much as 25 per cent. Only four to six pounds of processed seed were required to plant an acre, compared with eighteen to twenty pounds of whole seed.

Planting drills were adapted to handle the new, smaller seed and to drop it at spaced intervals instead of solidly in a row as had been the practice with the old seed. This opened the way for development of mechanical blocking and thinning. On smooth ground, an ordinary cultivator was found practical for drawing across the rows to eliminate excess plants. For ground with irrigation ditches between the rows, a thinner for use down the rows was developed. This consists of a series of small revolving blades, spaced according to a mathematical formula to remove excess plants and leave enough for a good stand. The same implement has been found practical for reducing the weeds that may grow between the remaining plants. Thus for the first time since the industry started, in-the-row thinning of beets and destruction of weeds between plants have been accomplished mechanically.

Processed seed and mechanical devices have reduced the amount of spring and summer hand labor by at least 50 per cent in some areas, and the labor still required can be done with a long-handled hoe, a real improvement over the short-handled hoe and finger-thinning formerly used. It was early recognized, however, that the final answer had not yet been found, because processing the seed ball did not always result in single-germ segments; two and sometimes three plants still occasionally grew from a single segment. And so the relentless search for a true single-germ or "monogerm" sugar beet seed continued.

Success on this score came in 1948, when two plants with the true monogerm character were found in an Oregon beet seed field. It was a momentous discovery, and followed examination of thousands of plants. The seed from those two Oregon plants was taken to the laboratory, and then came the slow, painstaking work of breeding the monogerm character into the seeds that would produce plants with high yield and disease-resistant qualities. By 1958 plant geneticists — in sugar company research departments, and state and federal experiment stations — had progressed enough in developing monogerm seed, with desirable characteristics, to permit significant commercial plantings. This seed, along with other developments — such as precision planters, mechanical and chemical weed killers, and constantly improving farming methods — provided the basis for forecasts that in time all phases of sugar beet production in the United States will be fully mechanized.

Other Advancements

Although perhaps not quite so spectacular as the recent growth of mechanization and the introduction of processed and monogerm seed, many other developments have taken place over the years. These include the continuous improvement of beet yields and sugar yields per acre, more effective use of both commercial and natural fertilizers, better irrigation methods, and the breeding of plants ever more resistant to diseases, insects and soil pests. All these have led to greater production of beets and sugar with the expenditure of fewer hours of human labor.

For example, in 1900 the average yield of beets was 6.4 tons per acre; in 1935, 10.4 tons; and in 1957, 17.7 tons per acre. Sugar produced per harvested acre, on the average, for the five-year period of 1950-54 was 16 per cent greater than during the five-year pre-war period of 1937-41. U.S. government experts on the subject estimated that in 1958 only about 3.5 man-days of work in the fields were required to produce the beets needed for making a ton of sugar, a reduction of almost one-third since 1948. Tests made by state colleges show that with complete mechanization of both thinning and harvesting, beets sufficient to make a ton of sugar may be produced with only 2.3 man-days of labor in the fields.

Still further increases in per-acre production in the United States can be expected from another development now on the threshold. Plant scientists are perfecting hybrid sugar beet seed on the same principles as the hybrids which so increased United States corn production per acre. Some of these new hybrid varieties have the monogerm character.

Beet Seed Now Produced in United States

Various reasons can be given for the constantly increasing production efficiency of the American sugar beet farmer — in addition to the traditional American attitude of looking at this year's new production record not as a final plateau but merely as a challenge, as something to be beaten next year.

One reason is that all sugar beet seed now used in the United States is a product of this country's research and thus is better adapted to American soils, climates and agricultural hazards. In the beginning of the beet sugar industry here and for many years thereafter, growers relied upon European sources for all or nearly all their seed. When supplies were virtually cut off during the first World War, commercial seed production started in the United States (in 1916) but was abandoned a few years after the war because of the amount of costly hand labor then involved. Again we turned to Europe for seed. The story of how sugar beet seed production became practical in the United States is a curious one.

The sugar beet plant is a biennial. In its first year it sinks a root and stores energy to be used the following year for producing seed. Normally the root is harvested the first year for sugar. But if permitted to grow a second year, the plant sends up a tall stalk which bears the seed. Under the European method of seed production, the roots were pulled from the ground in autumn of the

MECHANICAL THINNERS

Scientific advancements, both in seeds and machines, now permit mechanical thinning of young sugar beet plants and also removal of weeds in the rows — jobs formerly performed by hand. Photos here show two makes of machines with revolving blades. Cultivating between plants with mechanical equipment that moves down the row is a comparatively recent development in America's agricultural history.

first year of growth, stored through the winter, and replanted the following spring. Seed then grew on a thick, woody stalk. To harvest the seed, workers hacked off the stalks with heavy knives. All in all, this was hard work and decidedly costly under American wage scales. An American method to replace this procedure was found partly by accident, partly because of the acute observation of scientists.

Some years ago farmers in southeastern New Mexico attempted to grow sugar beets but with uniformly unsuccessful results. Thereupon experiments were conducted to find the best time of year for New Mexico plantings, simply by planting some beets in every one of the twelve months. It was probably a shock — certainly a disappointment at first — for the experimenters to discover that beets planted in the late fall months began, in the following spring, to send up seed stalks rather than to store sugar. Winter frosts had stopped the growth of the immature beets just as effectively as if they had been pulled up and siloed during the winter. But alert plant scientists with the New Mexico Agricultural Experiment Station and the United States Department of Agriculture recognized that this apparent nuisance was in reality a boon — not for sugar production but for seed production. The seed stalk produced by this over-wintering method was a triumph in itself. Only as thick as your thumb, it could be cut down with a mechanical mower. A tremendous amount of manual labor had thus been eliminated. Here was a new method of producing beet seed adaptable to areas having quite mild winters, yet with temperatures low enough to give the plant the "over-wintering" experience.

Beginning in the early 1930's, the American sugar beet seed industry was re-established, and grew rapidly as strains particularly adapted to the beet growing areas of this country were developed. Since 1941 the United States has imported no seed for commercial sugar beet production. Production of most of the seed used commercially in the United States — some 13 million pounds annually — is directed by two companies owned by groups of beet processing companies. Farmers grow the seed under contract with the seed companies.

Discovery of the over-wintering procedure has materially speeded development of improved seed strains. Several experiment stations now have refrigerated rooms where they can artificially induce winter temperatures to speed up the seed-producing process and thus reduce the time between generations of plants.

RESEARCH NEVER STOPS

Many of the strides made by the beet sugar industry in increasing its efficiency stem from the patient research of the plant scientists, whose laboratories are greenhouses and whose products are higher-yielding strains of sugar beets. Lights in a greenhouse at night (*above*) simulate sunshine to stretch the "growing day" for experimental plants. *Below*, mounted on the heads of common pins, are greatly magnified examples of (left to right) the normal multigerm seed ball, a "segmented" seed, and the new monogerm sugar beet seed, developed by plant scientists.

Close Relationship Between Grower and Sugar Company

Not the least of the reasons for continuous progress of the United States beet sugar industry is the close relationship between growers and the sugar companies. The grower buys his seed from the company, he grows beets under contract with the company, and all through the year the agricultural staff of the company provides a medium for exchange of information and ideas.

An important link in this information chain is the company fieldman, a highly-trained agricultural expert. He counsels with growers individually and at meetings, where he may show motion pictures and slides produced by the company to demonstrate improved methods of sugar beet production. Many companies also publish magazines for growers. These magazines regularly report on new and proven research developments and relate the experiences of growers with new practices.

One reason for the close relationship between producer and processing company is the unique contractual arrangement under which sugar beets are marketed. The amount a farmer receives per ton of beets is based on the sugar content of the beets and the final net return to the sugar company from the sale of sugar produced from the year's crop. This is the only case in the United States in which — on an industry-wide basis — the farmer's income for his crop bears a direct relationship to the net return received by the processing company from sale of the processed crop. This tends to give producer and processing company a mutuality of interest distinctive in American agriculture and industry.

Exchange of Scientific Information

A basic factor in the success and progress of any major industry today is the extent of research and the availability of information about scientific developments in the same or a related field. Each of the major beet sugar processing companies has its own research staff, and there is a full and free exchange of technical information among the technicians and scientists of the companies and of the state agricultural colleges and the Department of Agriculture.

A professional organization, the American Society of Sugar Beet Technologists, headquartered at Fort Collins, Colorado, serves as a forum for the exchange of information by holding national and regional meetings and publishing scientific papers. The

Society also maintains contacts with sugar beet scientists elsewhere in the world and disseminates information received from
them.

Another organization, the Beet Sugar Development Foundation, of Fort Collins, Colorado, advises state and federal experiment stations on the relative importance to the industry of proposed sugar beet projects and also channels research grants provided by the sugar companies.

Beet sugar companies also help support the Sugar Research
Foundation of New York City, which sponsors research to expand
knowledge of sugar and its role in nutrition and food technology.
Since sugar is a component of so many hundreds of commercially-
prepared foods, it is essential to learn in what quantities and under what conditions it can best be used to enhance the nutritional
values, flavor, and other factors of quality. Projects conducted
with the help of grants from the Foundation also include research
involving the use of sugar in non-food products, such as surface
coatings (paints and varnishes), plastics, agricultural chemicals,
detergents, fibers, films, solvents, explosives and adhesives. This
research suggests that the mechanical revolution which has so
transformed sugar beet production may, in the years to come,
be matched in the scope of its effects by a chemical revolution
leading to new uses of sugar in non-food products.

Chapter Six

EXTRACTING SUGAR
FROM THE BEET

At the height of the sugar-making campaign, a beet sugar factory presents a series of memorable impressions — the droning hum of motors; the splash of water in the beet-washing tanks; the whiz of wide conveyor belts; the whir of giant centrifugals; the clatter of sugar packaging machinery; and also, in contrast, the quiet watchfulness of factory technicians at the control panels of automatic and semi-automatic processing equipment.

Outside the factory rise piles of beets — in cool regions often covering acres, with ventilating tubes passing through the piles. Farmers bring more beets in a continuous stream of trucks. Various devices receive the beets — elevated trestles, power-driven belts and portable machines that deliver truck loads to the piles.

Long freight trains roll into the bustling factory yard with still more beets from outlying stations. The brimful cars climb the trestles, or dump beets into bins or into "wet hoppers" — concrete trenches from which beets are flumed into the factory.

Beside the factory are stocks of coke, limerock and, unless oil or gas is the principal fuel, huge piles of coal. On the average it requires thirty-five pounds of coke and limerock and sixty pounds of coal to produce a hundred pounds of sugar.

The visitor to the factory during the campaign sees on the one hand thousands of tons of beets arriving; on the other, freight cars being loaded with pure, refined sugar from the warehouse; and in between, a wide panorama of industrial activity.

The Basic Processes

The work of extracting sugar from the beet consists of basic processes that sound simple enough: the sugar first is soaked from

UNLOADING SUGAR BEETS AT THE FACTORY

During harvest, sugar beets arrive continuously at the factory — some by truck directly from nearby farms and some by long trains from receiving stations at outlying points. After being weighed, each truck is unloaded swiftly (*above*) and the beets are piled to await processing. When hopper-type railroad cars are used (*below*), the cars may be unloaded directly into a flume which floats the beets into the processing plant.

$3,000,000 WORTH OF SUGAR BEETS

When the weather is warm, sugar beets are processed within 24 hours of the time they reach the factory, and the harvest is planned to keep pace with factory operations. As cooler fall weather comes, in most parts of the country the beets are harvested as fast as possible and then stored in huge piles in the factory yard until they can be processed. Factory operations in cool climates continue for several weeks after the harvest is completed.

This air view of a factory storage area shows $3,000,000 worth of sugar beets awaiting processing. The pyramid-shaped rows in the background are beets that were hauled in by some of the 14,000 railroad cars utilized during the harvest in this particular area. The grooved piles in the foreground represent a portion of the 100,000 truck loads delivered to this factory. Ventilating tubes circulate cool night air through the piles to prevent spoilage. In the extreme right foreground are two white piles of limerock which will be used for making milk of lime, an essential ingredient for the sugar-purifying process. The single black pile at the extreme right is coal for the factory boilers.

the beet in liquid form; the resulting juice then is purified, concentrated, and crystallized; and finally the crystals are separated from the remaining liquid.

Actually, sugar chemistry is infinitely complex, and intricate engineering problems are involved. Specific processes include such operations as diffusion, precipitation, filtration, evaporation, crystallization and centrifuging. In fact, most of the important so-called "unit processes" of chemical engineering are represented in a beet sugar factory.

While details of methods and equipment vary somewhat among factories and in different parts of the country, the following description may be considered to be a general outline of the processes that take place in a typical factory.

Cleaning and Slicing the Beets

Cleanliness is a watchword throughout a sugar factory, and cleanliness begins with clean beets. Most of the bits of earth that cling to the beet when it is pulled from the ground are removed before the beets are delivered to the storage area, bins, or flumes.

Water in the flumes, carrying the beets into the factory, washes off more dirt and softens what may remain. "Trash catchers" of various types remove whatever other foreign matter may still be mixed with the beets, such as bits of grass or leaves. Still the cleaning process is not complete.

As they enter the final washer, the beets are subjected to a high pressure spray of water, then swished around by rotating paddles or pulled on an endless chain system moving counter to a stream of water. Another high pressure spray rinses the beets as they leave the washer.

The thoroughly cleansed beets are now ready for the first stage of actual processing. They fall through a hopper into revolving knives, which cut the beets into thin strips that look something like "shoe-string" potatoes. The slices, which are V-shaped, are known as *cossettes*, one of the many French terms used in the industry. Factory workers call them *chips*.

Removing Sugar by Diffusion

Now comes the process of removing the sugar from the cossettes. This is accomplished by soaking the thin beet strips in hot water, in a huge container called a *diffuser*. This action takes the sugar from the tiny plant cells and diffuses it through the hot water. Fresh hot water first reaches the cossettes from which the most sugar has been taken and then moves, with its temperature carefully controlled, through a series of compartments in a direction opposite to the movement of the cossettes. As it progresses through the diffuser, the liquid removes additional fractions of the sugar in the chips and finally contains enough sugar to be called *raw juice.*

In a typical modern factory the huge diffuser, which weighs some three hundred tons, is run by one man who controls the operation principally by push buttons.

With their sugar removed, the cossettes now are called *beet pulp* and are conveyed to the pulp dryer or to the storage place for wet pulp. The *raw juice,* which has a sugar content of 10 to 15 per cent but also contains some non-sugar substances, now goes to the purification stages.

Purification of the Juice; Evaporation

Two main processes are used in removing the non-sugar substances from the juice. First these substances are precipitated or coagulated. This is followed by a filtering process which removes the non-sugar substances.

Milk of lime and carbon dioxide gas are used in the precipitation stage. Both the lime and the gas are made by burning limerock and coke in a lime kiln. The milk of lime, a suspension of lime in water, absorbs or coagulates part of the non-sugars and makes them insoluble; the carbon dioxide in turn makes the lime insoluble. When the juice is run through batteries of filter presses, then, the lime is filtered out and with it go the non-sugars.

To make doubly sure of removing impurities, the raw juice twice goes through this carbonating and filtering process. Now known as *thin juice,* it requires thickening before sugar crystals will form readily.

This is done by running the thin juice through a series of five evaporators. Called multiple-effect evaporators, they provide an example of one of the many economies that have been effected to achieve efficiency of beet sugar production. Because the process of extracting sugar requires quantities of both steam and electric power, the factory has huge boilers and electric generators. The live steam from the boilers is used first to operate the generators. Then it is used five times over in the evaporators to concentrate the thin juice to a thick juice. Of course the steam loses some of its heat in each evaporator. To compensate for this, the pressure

SPIC AND SPAN FACTORIES

Most stages of sugar beet processing take place in closed, gleaming white equipment. *Above* are vacuum "pans" — huge containers in which sugar crystals are formed after purification and evaporation of the sugar-containing juices. Crystallization is started in a super-saturated solution by "seeding" with pulverized sugar. Crystal growth is controlled by skilled technicians.

in each succeeding evaporator is decreased; this enables the liquid to boil at a lower temperature.

The concentrated juice coming from the evaporators is called, appropriately enough, *thick juice*. It now has a sugar content of 50 to 65 per cent — instead of the 10 to 15 per cent it had in the raw juice stage. Further filtering of the juice plus the addition of intermediate and raw sugars produced later in the process yields a sparkling, clear liquid known as *standard liquor*.

Forming Sugar Crystals

The next major stage in the processing is to change the sugar in the juice from liquid to crystal form.

Crystallization is achieved by boiling the standard liquor in huge tanks called vacuum pans. To prevent burning and caramelization, the boiling must be done at a comparatively low temperature; hence a high vacuum is necessary. The standard liquor is boiled until it reaches a state of supersaturation. A sugar solution is said to be supersaturated when there is a greater ratio of dissolved sugar to water than could normally exist at that temperature. Then, by injecting a small amount of pulverized sugar, the liquid is *seeded* — and sugar crystals begin to form.

Control of the crystallization process is an art, and the process is conducted by a skilled technician. By regulating the vacuum and temperature, by adding more standard liquor when necessary, by using steam, he governs the growth of crystals until they reach the proper size. The sugar boiler takes frequent samples from the vacuum pans and examines the crystals under a magnifying device. The instant the crystals reach the desired size, the operator stops the crystallizing process.

The mass in the vacuum pan now is a thick mixture of crystals and syrup and although it is brown in color it is, strangely enough, known as *white fillmass*.

Separating Crystals from Syrup

The next step is spectacular. The fillmass is poured into high-speed centrifugal machines. Essentially the centrifugal is a huge revolving metal basket, perforated with extremely fine holes and surrounded by a stationary outer shell. After the fillmass is poured into the basket, the basket whirls at a peripheral speed of more than two miles a minute. This action throws the fillmass to the sides of the basket, and the brown syrup passes through the holes while the white crystals remain inside the basket. As the machine spins, the brown color changes quickly to sparkling white. A jet of hot water sprays on the sugar, and this also passes through the perforations of the basket, washing off the last traces of the syrup.

The wet sugar now passes to granulators, where it is dried in a current of warm air. Then it is screened to sort crystals according to size and sent to bins or huge silos for later packaging or removal for delivery in bulk.

The syrup that has been separated from the sugar crystals and expelled through the holes in the sides of the centrifugal basket still contains considerable sugar in liquid form. This syrup undergoes two more boilings and centrifugings, during which it yields the intermediate and raw sugars that are added back to the thick juice for further processing.

Processing Molasses

The syrup thrown off by the third centrifuging is called molasses. It still contains some sugar in liquid form which cannot be economically recovered by additional boiling and centrifuging. A method known as the Steffen process, however, is used for recovering more sugar from molasses.

This process involves adding finely ground lime to a molasses solution. The sugar forms an insoluble compound with the lime, known as calcium saccharate. This is separated by filtration, thoroughly washed and returned to the sugar-making process, where it is mixed with incoming diffusion juice. The lime in the saccharate serves the same purpose in clarifying the diffusion juice as does the milk of lime.

Processors have also developed a way to extract still more sugar from molasses after it has gone through the Steffen process — by using barium hydroxide to precipitate additional sugar.

By-Products of the Sugar Factory

Since the beginning of the beet sugar industry in Europe, the value of beet pulp as a livestock feed has been recognized. Beet pulp consists of the cossettes — the sliced beets — after the recoverable sugar has been removed. Pulp and the agricultural uses of molasses have been discussed in Chapter Four.

Molasses also has a variety of industrial uses. It is used extensively in the fermentation industry, particularly in eastern states,

TWO MILES A MINUTE

One of the most spectacular of all beet sugar factory operations comes near
the end of the processing, and takes place in a machine called a centrifugal,
pictured *above*. After final purification and evaporation of sugar-containing
juices, sugar crystals are formed by controlled boiling. The resulting substance, called fillmass, contains both white sugar crystals and a brown molasses. To separate the crystals from the liquid molasses, the fillmass is
poured into the large metal basket of the centrifugal. The basket, which has
tiny holes in its wall, whirls at a speed reaching two miles a minute or more
at the outside edge. This action spins the liquid through the holes, while
the crystals are held inside the basket. The observer sees a thick, brown
substance enter the basket and seemingly change, in an instant, to sparkling white sugar crystals. Many beet sugar factories now have automatic
centrifugals.

where it is used in the manufacture of citric acid, yeast, antibiotics, and other products.

A product of increasing importance in the household and in the food industry, monosodium glutamate, also stems from a by-product of the beet sugar factory. Concentrated Steffen filtrate, once considered a waste product of the Steffen process of extracting sugar from beet molasses, now is used in the manufacture of monosodium glutamate — which intensifies the flavor and increases the delectability of many foods. This process produces further by-products from the beet — potash fertilizer and high protein livestock feed.

A Thousand Laboratory Tests Every Day

With its multitude of processes, the sugar factory has been described as a chemical laboratory. But it has a laboratory of its own, too, where chemists and technicians conduct over a thousand tests every twenty-four hours to maintain the high quality of the factory's principal product— sugar.

These tests cover a wide range, and include testing the whiteness of the sugar, the size of the crystals, and sugar's behavior in certain uses, such as syrup-making and candy-making. The result is an assurance to the consuming public that beet sugar is 99.9+ per cent pure sucrose, unsurpassed for any food use.

Pure Beet Sugar Available in All Forms

Most of the sugar sold in the United States is in granulated form. Crystals are made in various sizes to meet special needs. (Incidentally, size of crystals has no bearing on quality.) Also to meet the needs of consumers, granulated beet sugar is packaged in many sizes of containers — from quarter-ounce single-service packets for restaurant and institutional use to 100-pound bags for industrial use. The most popular home sizes are five-pound and ten-pound paper bags and one-pound cartons.

Many industrial users — such as canners, candy-makers, bakers and soft drink bottlers — prefer to receive sugar in bulk or in liquid form. Beet sugar companies meet these requirements by shipping both bulk and liquid sugar in specially-lined railroad cars and trucks. Devices have even been developed in the beet sugar industry for dissolving granulated sugar in water while the dry sugar is being unloaded from a truck or railroad car at the customer's plant.

Liquid beet sugar is always prepared by dissolving pure granulated sugar in water. Thus it is sugar that has been carried all the way through the final purification process.

Beet sugar is available in still other forms — cubes, tablets, powdered, and brown — to satisfy completely the discriminating tastes of Americans for the highest quality product in a variety of types.

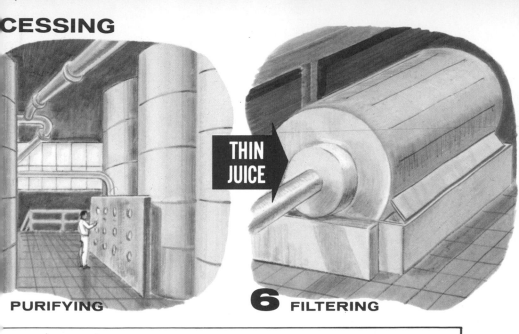

CESSING

PURIFYING

THIN JUICE

6 FILTERING

DRYING

12 PACKAGING

SUGAR

PURE BEET SUGAR

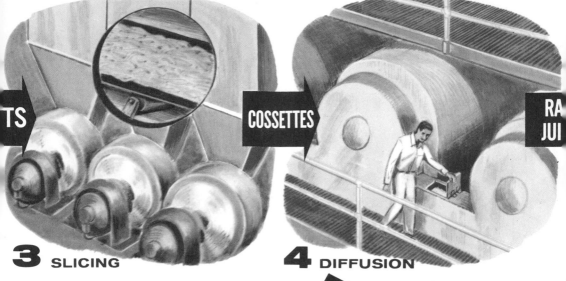

TS

COSSETTES

**RA
JUI**

3 SLICING   **4** DIFFUSION

essing,
settes.
moved

mois-
ocess-
feed.)
car-
idified

ystals
Crys-
ses —
The
iners,

**BEET
PULP**

MOLASSES

9 CRYSTALIZING   **10** CENTRIFUGING

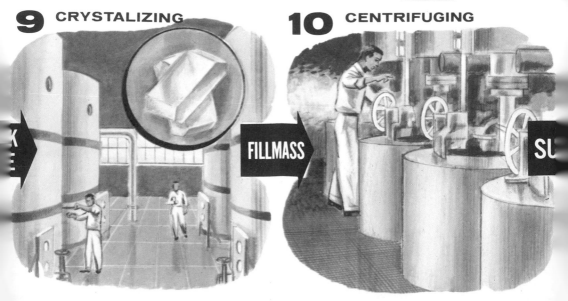

K

FILLMASS

SU

1 THE SUGAR BEET

2 WASHING

ILLUSTRATED PROCESSING STEPS

I. Sugar beets arrive at the factory without crown and green leaves. **2.** In preparation f beets are washed thoroughly. **3.** Then, razor-sharp knives slice the beets into thin strips ca **4.** Through diffusion — a process which involves soaking the cossettes in hot water — the sug in liquid form called raw juice.

(With sugar removed, the cossettes are called beet pulp. This may be fed to livestock while ture may be removed by pressure and heat. Often beet molasses, from a later stage in the s ing, is added to the pulp before drying. In dried form, sugar beet pulp is also a highly desirable l

5. The raw juice leaves the diffuser and goes through various purifying processes. Milk of bon dioxide gas precipitate (solidify) non-sugar substances in the juice. **6.** Filtering removes particles and thus removes non-sugars. Carbonating and filtering are repeated.

7. The purified juice is thickened by evaporating excess moisture. **8.** More filtering takes pla are formed in the thick juice by boiling in huge vacuum "pans" and seeding with pulverized su tals are separated from the remaining liquid by whirling in high-speed centrifuges. (The liquid is used for by-products, including livestock feed.) **II.** Crystals are dried and sorted according to pure sugar then is packaged or stored in large bins. Pure beet sugar is available in many sizes and also in bulk and liquid form.

7 EVAPORATING

8 MORE FILTERING

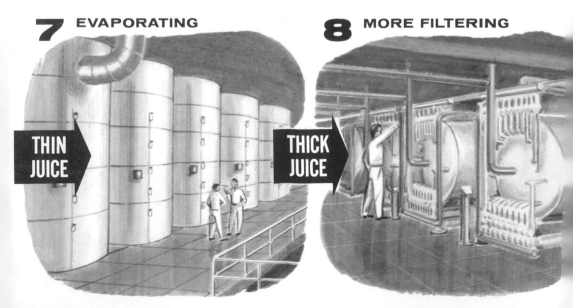

THIN JUICE

THICK JUICE

Chapter Seven

THE IMPORTANT ROLE OF SUGAR IN THE DIET

Sugar appeals to most people for one simple and obvious reason — it tastes good. By itself and in other foods, sugar's delightful sweetness has a universal attraction. It makes other foods taste better. It counteracts less pleasing flavors of some foods, and enhances the naturally pleasant flavor of others. In cookery, sugar also improves the appearance of other foods — makes them look more appetizing as well as taste better.

To nutritionists, still further reasons exist for sugar's important place in the diet. The reasons are found in sugar's role as a highly concentrated *energy* food.

Classes of Food

Food researchers have divided foods into various classes according to their chemical composition, and have studied the functions that each performs in the human body. A well-rounded diet, they have found, consists of an adequate supply of *all* the essential food classes, which are proteins, carbohydrates, fats, minerals and vitamins — plus water. Each of these supplies certain necessities for building and maintaining a strong, healthy and energetic body.

Proteins are necessary to build and maintain organ, bone and muscle tissue. Carbohydrates are the most common and versatile source of energy. Fats have abundant calories and are sources of certain fatty acids and vitamins the body requires. Minerals and vitamins in various ways regulate body functions and enable the body to utilize its food more efficiently. To be well-balanced nutritionally, an individual's diet should contain all these food factors in proper proportion.

Sugar is a pure carbohydrate, and therefore a concentrated energy food.

How the Body Uses Sugar

The way in which the body uses sugar demonstrates one of the remarkable cycles of nature.

Beet sugar, like maple and cane sugar, is sucrose — which is classified as a *disaccharide*. In the digestion of sugar, the human body first converts the disaccharides to the monosaccharides, dextrose and levulose, commonly called simple sugars. These simple sugars enter the bloodstream, and may be carried to tissues and used immediately for energy. The portion that is not required at once is carried to the body's "storehouses," the liver and muscles, where the simple sugars are converted to glycogen, or animal starch. The liver stores the glycogen until it is needed to supply energy. Then the glycogen is converted to blood sugar and poured back into the bloodstream. The quantity of blood sugar normally present in the blood may vary widely among individuals.

The blood carries the blood sugar to the muscles, which are also capable of manufacturing and storing glycogen. When energy is required for muscular action, the glycogen supplies it. During the expenditure of energy the glycogen in the muscles is broken down first to glucose, and finally to carbon dioxide and water. The carbon dioxide is carried by the blood to the lungs and then exhaled. The water is thrown off by the lungs, by the kidneys, and as perspiration of the skin.

Thus the sugar, which was originally manufactured by growing plants from carbon dioxide and water, together with the sun's energy, becomes carbon dioxide and water again when the energy is used by the human body.

The Need for an Energy Food

Modern scientific research on foods and how the body uses them has disproved and still is disproving many false ideas and prejudices that formerly were held about sugar and its place in the diet. Once sugar was virtually banned from the athlete's training table. Today swimmers and other athletes are deliberately given sugar during an event to gets its quick energy. It has been learned that "staleness" can result from a deficiency in blood sugar, which is used up rapidly during exercise.

SUGAR FOR ENERGY AND FLAVOR

A sugar-containing snack (*above*) helps give youngsters the energy they use so rapidly. In fact, everyone needs energy foods for work or play. Sugar provides energy in a form more readily available for human use than any other food. Sugar also enhances the flavor of other foods, and has certain preserving qualities. Beet sugar is the favorite of thousands of housewives for canning and jelly-making (*below*).

PURE
BEET
SUGAR

When quick energy is needed for work or play, sugar supplies it faster than any other food. Physiological chemists say the body begins to use sugar within five minutes after it is eaten.

The value of sugar to the growing child is also coming to be recognized more fully. Active children have high energy-food requirements, and foods high in sugar content are helpful.

Sugar need not replace any other essential nutrients in the diet. After vitamin, mineral and protein needs are met, the body needs still more energy for its daily tasks and to maintain proper weight and vitality. Usually the basic daily requirements for nutrients, other than calories, can be met by foods furnishing less than two-thirds of the body's energy needs. Sugar is a means of supplying part of this energy deficit, and of combining the sources of other nutrients such as vitamins, minerals and proteins into delicious foods that add zest, satisfaction and balance to meals.

Sugar — an Aid to Reducing

Research of recent years has disproved many of the mistaken conceptions formerly held about diets for people who want to reduce weight. It has been learned that the sensible, healthful and *effective* way to reduce weight is to cut *down* on the total quantity of food and not necessarily cut *out* any food.

Some of the most enlightening research on this subject has been conducted over a period of years at Harvard University in projects directed by Fredrick J. Stare, M.D. The role of sugar in a reducing diet was described by Dr. Stare and Julia Lyons, M.S., also of the Department of Nutrition, Harvard School of Public Health, in an article they published in the January, 1956, issue of *McCall's* magazine. They wrote:

"Sugar is a quick-energy food and pleasant to take. For centuries it has been used to make other foods more palatable. It does not contain any appreciable amount of vitamins and minerals, furnishing calories only. But a level teaspoonful has only about 16[*] calories, not enough to make much difference. Even people on a severe reducing diet can afford to put a teaspoonful of sugar in their tea or coffee three or four times a day.

"In a three-year study of overweight people made by Harvard's Department of Nutrition, it was found that those who gave up sugar entirely lost no more weight than people who used sugar. Moreover, a small dose of sugar is a quick and effective way of raising the blood-sugar level and hence reducing appetite. When

[*] The official U.S. standard teaspoon of sugar contains 18 calories.

we say to a small child 'Johnny, put down that cookie — it's too soon before supper, and you'll spoil your appetite,' we're stating a fact. A small amount of almost any food taken shortly before a meal will often help dieters stay the hunger pangs and keep them from overeating at meals. A between-meal nibble can be a help to many dieters provided, of course, they reduce the size of their meals by the amount taken in the nibble."

The article concludes:

"So if it's desirable for you to take off a few pounds — or many — the best way to do it is to cut *down* on the total quantity of food and not necessarily to cut *out* any. A balanced diet, including meat, eggs, milk, cereal products, vegetables and fruits — none of them in excessive quantity — is the healthiest, best and most effective one. And that includes bread, potatoes and sugar as well as any other three wholesome foods. They provide nutrients and energy important to body needs, they are not excessively high in calories, and we find them everywhere in abundance and at low cost."

Other Health Factors

Extensive research has failed to support the popular belief that sugar is uniquely responsible for tooth decay. Dental health involves many things, including heredity, diet, bony structure of the jaws, climate — even the composition of drinking water. A reasonable conclusion from research on this subject is that sound teeth require a nutritionally well-balanced and well-rounded diet that promotes general health, plus, of course, sensible health habits, including care and frequent cleansing of the teeth.

Certain so-called sugar "substitutes" — usually derived from coal-tar — are sometimes promoted for use by the calorie-conscious. Federal and many state Food and Drug laws require that the manufacturer of any product containing a synthetic sweetener warn the purchaser by including this statement on the label: "Should be used only by persons who must restrict their intake of ordinary sweets." The truth is that there really is no genuine substitute for sugar.

Sugar in Cookery

Sugar usually is combined with other foods, and its effect in improving the flavor of foods, making them more appealing to the taste, is well known. Yet sugar — sucrose — has other important attributes, in addition to sweetness, that make it invaluable to the housewife in her kitchen.

Sugar offsets to a certain extent an excess of salty flavor; the housewife almost automatically reaches for the sugar when she oversalts the soup. Sugar also counteracts an acid flavor, and makes the true flavor of fruits, for example, stand out. The addition of a small amount of sugar while cooking vegetables emphasizes their "fresh" flavor.

Another reaction of sugar in most of the processes of sugar cookery is called "hydrolysis." This action, which occurs when sugar is heated with water, results in breaking down the single sucrose molecule into two molecules of the simple sugars, dextrose and levulose. (It will be recalled that this is what happens to sucrose during digestion in the human body.) In cookery, "hydrolysis" — or "inversion" — decreases the tendency of sugar to crystallize from thick syrups or jellies.

Sugar's generous solubility in water is also important to the housewife, particularly the fact that sugar may remain completely dissolved in varying degrees of saturation — that is, in solutions of varying degrees of sweetness.

Another important quality is sugar's ability to "caramelize" or turn brown. When dry sugar is heated to a sufficiently high temperature, it melts. As it melts, the color changes, first to yellow and then to brown. What happens, chemically, is that the hydrogen and oxygen are gradually being passed off as water vapor, leaving colored substances with the pleasant and distinctive flavor we call "caramel." This browning characteristic of sugar adds flavor as well as a pleasing brown color to the crust of baked goods which contain sugar.

Still another use of sugar in cookery is as a preservative. A preservative is any substance that retards or stops the growth of organisms that spoil food. Sugar performs this action when it is present in sufficient concentration. Microorganisms such as certain bacteria and yeast require water in order to grow. Sugar stops this growth by drawing the water from their cells by a process called *osmosis*.

All these valuable qualities of sugar in cookery apply equally to all sugar — sucrose — no matter from which plant the sucrose is extracted.

Thus we see that sugar plays an important role in the diet for many reasons. One of course is the natural appeal of sugar's delicious flavor. Sugar is an essential ingredient of many food preparations— enhancing the flavor of other foods and performing other valuable functions in cookery. And sugar is a highly concentrated *energy* food. It provides energy — the basis of life itself — in a form that the body readily and quickly converts to human energy. Small wonder it is, then, that nations over the globe regard a dependable sugar supply as essential to their welfare.

Chapter Eight

THE SUGAR ACT
AND HOW IT WORKS

World-Wide Controls

Sugar supplies and markets are of deep concern to nations throughout the world. This fact has led to widespread national and international controls. The law that regulates sugar production and marketing in the United States — the Sugar Act — should be considered against this background of nearly universal governmental and inter-governmental supervision of the sugar trade.

National sugar legislation, in effect in virtually every country on the globe, takes various forms, depending upon the needs and interests of the nation involved. Importing nations seek to assure a sugar supply in time of crisis, usually by encouraging at least some domestic sugar production and making special arrangements for additional supplies from nations that export. Exporting nations, particularly those whose economies depend primarily upon sugar production, seek to obtain assured markets for their sugar. Methods and machinery to attain these aims vary widely.

For example, United Kingdom sugar regulations involve a Commonwealth Agreement which fixes prices on part of the sugar brought to the U.K. from members of the British Commonwealth of Nations; a protective program of price-fixing on domestically-produced sugar; tariffs; and a government-industry understanding regarding prices to consumers.

Among other things, the French system includes import licensing, tariffs, fixed prices to producers, a ceiling on the price to consumers, an export subsidy, a 12 per cent tax on the wholesale price of sugar, and a 10 per cent social security tax on sugar beets.

In some countries, all imports are handled by the government itself rather than by private individuals or firms.

In Cuba, the world's largest sugar exporter, the Cuban Sugar Stabilization Institute, composed of both government and sugar trade representatives, exercises rigid control over production and marketing. Among various devices used in the Cuban system are price pooling, a production tax, a tariff, and an export tax that is reduced for sugar cargoes leaving the country in Cuban-owned vessels.

The United States sugar program establishes marketing quotas for the various domestic producing areas as well as import quotas. A sizable portion of the annual American sugar market is reserved for foreign countries, particularly for Cuba. A unique part of the United States program is a tax and conditional payment system for enforcing various restrictions and controls on the domestic industry. The tariff now plays only a minor part in the American system.

About one-third of total world sugar production enters the channels of international trade. More than one-half of this amount is regulated by various preferential arrangements between specific exporting and importing nations. The so-called "world free market" is a residual one, made up of less than one-half the total sugar moving in international trade. Most of the sugar supplies for the "world free market" come from exporting countries that participate in the International Sugar Agreement. In the fall of 1958 a new International Sugar Agreement was negotiated, effective in 1959, with participation indicated by all countries that regularly export sugar to the world market.

Obviously sugar is one of the most regulated commodities in the world — and all over the world. Recognition of this fact is essential for understanding why the United States, also, has a comprehensive sugar program. Understanding of the American program will be aided further by consideration of our own sugar laws that preceded the present program, and the events that led to first adopting its principles in 1934.

Early American Laws Concerning Sugar

For 145 years before the principles of the present program evolved in legislative form, Congress had enacted other laws affecting sugar. One of the first bills passed by the first Congress in the first administration of George Washington concerned sugar. It was a raw sugar tariff of 1 cent a pound, enacted in 1789 to help provide income for the new Republic, and at the start accounted for about 20 per cent of all import duties.

Initially intended solely as a revenue-producing measure, the tariff became primarily a protective device as sugar-producing areas became part of or closely associated with our growing nation. The cane growers of Louisiana were the first to receive this protection, when the Louisiana Territory was purchased from France in 1803. Later, in 1876, the Kingdom of Hawaii was given tariff protection on the American market by a reciprocal trade treaty which permitted Hawaiian sugar to enter the United States duty-free. When the United States beet sugar industry came into existence with the first success in California in 1879, beet sugar automatically received the protection of the tariff already in effect.

The sugar tariff, with varying rates, remained in force without interruption from its enactment in 1789 until 1890. In the latter year the United States Treasury found itself in the fortunate position of having a surplus, and Congress reduced the tariff on refined sugar from $3\frac{1}{2}$ cents a pound to $\frac{1}{2}$ cent a pound, and completely repealed the raw sugar tariff, which then was $2\frac{1}{4}$ cents a pound.

To ease the severe jolt this action would have given the domestic sugar industry, Congress provided for payment of a bounty of 2 cents on each pound of domestically-produced sugar. Repeal of the tariff of course removed the preferential position of Hawaiian sugar, and a bounty could not logically be paid to its producers because the Islands then were not a United States Territory. As a result, the price of Hawaiian sugar fell sharply, causing economic disturbances and general unrest which led to the fall of Queen Liliuokalani's monarchy in 1893 and establishment of the Republic of Hawaii in the following year.

Congress in 1894 abolished the bounty for American producers and enacted another sugar tariff — again exempting Hawaiian sugar from the duty. The tariff, at various rates, was our sole implement of national sugar policy from 1894 to 1934.

Events of 1894 to 1934

Certain events occurred early in this forty-year period that appreciably widened America's sphere of influence and responsibility in the world and created changes in our sources of sugar supply that still affect America's sugar situation today.

The first occurred in 1898. The Republic of Hawaii was annexed to the United States as the Territory of Hawaii, and thus became classified as a domestic rather than foreign sugar producing area. The Spanish-American War of 1898 brought two other heavy sugar producers — Puerto Rico and the Philippine Islands — into the "domestic area" category as possessions of the United States. Puerto Rican sugar was admitted without duty, beginning in 1901. Duty on Philippine sugar was reduced gradually until by 1913 the duty was eliminated. (Philippine sugar was to remain duty-free until after the Philippines were given their independence following World War II. The Philippine Trade Agreement Revision Act of 1955 provided for gradual reinstitution of duty, beginning in 1956.)

The Spanish-American War gave Cuba her independence. Under the 1902 Convention of Commercial Reciprocity, the duty on United States imports from the new Republic of Cuba, including sugar, was automatically placed at 20 per cent under the full duty rate in return for a similar duty preference on Cuban imports from the United States. This duty preference spurred sugar production in the new republic and in the next ten years, largely with the aid of American investors, the output of Cuban sugar more than doubled. By 1913 virtually all other foreign sugar had been pushed out of the American market.

For the sugar trade generally throughout the world, the period from 1894 to 1934 was largely a series of ups and downs. A publication of the United States Department of Agriculture, *The United States Sugar Program,* describes that era in these words: "The history of the sugar industry during that period is a sequence of stable earnings, wild prosperity, severe but short-lived depression, temporary recovery, and prolonged depression in that order."

For the sugar consumer it was also a period of chaotic conditions — ranging from times when more sugar was available than possibly could be consumed and prices were extremely low, to times when sugar was among the scarcest of commodities and prices skyrocketed to heights beyond reason. These conditions of feast and famine worked hardships upon the housewife and also upon the industrial user, who didn't know whether to stock his warehouses to be sure of a supply and to protect against a sudden price rise — or to keep inventories low to avoid a quick and drastic decline in inventory value.

A marketing situation arose in the United States in 1920 which dramatically illustrates the uncertainties of the period. For a time that year, foreign sugar interests, principally Cuban, had control of the market, and retail prices shot up to 27 cents a pound — higher than at any time since the Civil War period. Prices plummeted by the end of the year, causing almost as much hardship for some consumers as the sharp rise had caused. This fluctuation was particularly disturbing to industrial sugar users. They had been obliged to buy at high prices to maintain the output of their sugar-containing products, and now they found their inventories suddenly and disastrously devalued.

The sugar business, both foreign and domestic, seemed to recover for a while after that wild year of 1920, and then entered a long period of difficulties. A rising tide of nationalism in Europe was one of the influences that spurred production there. Elsewhere in the world, also, production expanded and exceeded effective demand. The severe business depression that gripped the world in the late 1920's and early 1930's aggravated existing difficulties in the sugar business. Both the Cuban industry — more than half of it then owned by American capital — and the domestic industry were in serious trouble.

Efforts were made to remedy the situation by further increases in the tariff. In 1930 the duty rate was raised to 2 cents a pound on Cuban sugar and $2\frac{1}{2}$ cents on other foreign sugar. Under the circumstances prevailing at that time, the higher tariff rates proved to be of only short-term benefit to domestic producers. By 1933 they were in desperate financial straits, as were Cuban producers. The Cuban industry, after paying shipping costs, was receiving only $\frac{1}{2}$ cent a pound for raw sugar sold in New York.

In a letter to the President, in April of 1933, the United States Tariff Commission pointed out that something in addition to a tariff was needed, and suggested that a marketing quota system be developed. The letter made repeated references to Cuba and offered the opinion that a quota system would permit a reduction in the tariff which would be beneficial to the Cuban economy.

Purposes of the Sugar Act

To find a new approach to the sugar problem, the executive and legislative branches of the government held many consultations with sugar producers, processors and consumers — with groups concerned with all phases of the sugar trade. Finally, the new approach was evolved and embodied in the Jones-Costigan Act, which the President signed on May 9, 1934. Although this legislation did not officially bear the name, Sugar Act, until it was amended in 1937, the law passed in 1934 was in reality the first comprehensive U.S. Sugar Act, and its fundamental principles and techniques are still part of the law now in effect.

The Act had these principal purposes:

1. To assure American consumers an adequate supply of sugar at reasonable prices.
2. To encourage foreign trade.
3. To provide a healthy economic climate for a competitive domestic sugar industry.

These fundamental purposes have not changed, although the Act has been re-enacted and amended several times.

Estimate of Annual Sugar Requirements

The methods of achieving these aims also have remained the same through various amendments to the Act.

The basis of the entire program — the foundation upon which the other parts of the program rest — is an estimate of our annual sugar needs made by the Secretary of Agriculture. Officially, this is called the determination of sugar requirements of consumers.

On the size of this estimate depends the total of all marketing quotas which the law assigns, according to a definite formula, to the various foreign countries and domestic producing areas that sell sugar on the American market. For domestic areas the quotas, in turn, are allotted to individual sugar companies when necessary to assure orderly marketing. The size of the domestic quotas is a determining factor in establishing the number of acres of sugar beets and sugar cane that may be planted in any particular year. All these factors are governed by the size of the estimate of consumers' requirements.

Recognizing the importance of the estimate to the whole sugar program, the law specifically names the factors the Secretary must consider in arriving at his determination. Each December he makes his first estimate for the following year, and as a starting base for his calculations he must use the amount of sugar that entered the channels of trade in the United States for the year ending the preceding October 31.

He is then required to adjust this figure by taking into consideration any variations from normal inventories, changes in consumption likely to take place because of changes in population and demand conditions, and the level and trend of consumer purchasing power. In addition he must consider the relationship between the sugar price he expects to prevail, and the general cost of living in the United States — as compared with the relationship between the price of sugar and the cost of living from 1947 to 1949.

As a matter of practice, the Secretary holds a public hearing in the fall of each year to obtain the views of interested parties as to how these various factors should be applied and weighed in the light of current circumstances.

The Secretary's objective in all these considerations is to arrive at a figure which will result in providing a supply of sugar that will be consumed at prices reasonable to consumers and fair to producers. As the law states it, the Secretary's estimate of consumption requirements "shall be made so as to protect the welfare of consumers and of those engaged in the domestic sugar industry."

Although he makes his initial estimate for any year during December of the year before, he may and usually does change the estimate any time during the year he feels a change up or down will help achieve the purposes of the Sugar Act. The Secretary does not have the power to fix sugar prices, but because his estimate of consumption requirements fixes the available supply of sugar, his action does of course influence prices. The flexibility which the Secretary has in establishing and modifying the estimate of consumption requirements ordinarily makes it possible to stabilize sugar prices, especially raw sugar prices, within a rather narrow range. Should prices appear to be getting out of this range or likely to do so, the Secretary may adjust the estimate in order to get the price effect of larger or smaller supplies.

Marketing Quotas

Once the amount of sugar consumers will need in a year is determined, the next step is to determine who is going to provide it. This is done by a system of marketing quotas, which allocate the total needs among the various foreign countries and domestic areas from which we obtain sugar. The pattern of the quotas is established by Congress, and the Secretary must follow the formula set forth in the law when he calculates the quotas.

When the first Act was passed in 1934, the quota pattern followed the general pattern of actual marketing for the immediately preceding years. About 55 per cent of the total was allocated to domestic areas, and about 45 per cent was reserved for foreign countries. The exact pattern for specific areas has varied with different amendments of the Act. Amendments effective in 1948, for example, tied domestic areas to fixed quotas while annual increases in the market were given to foreign countries, principally Cuba. Amendments passed in 1956 permitted domestic areas to market 55 per cent of subsequent increases in the market.

The beet sugar producing area in 1958 had a quota amounting to nearly one-fourth of total U.S. consumption — which was equal to about 40 per cent of the total basic quotas of all the domestic producing areas.

Marketing Allotments

The next phase of the program is the marketing allotment, which breaks down the quota of a domestic area among the various sugar companies in the area. The Secretary allots the quota among the companies in an area when this appears necessary for assuring an orderly and adequate flow of sugar or for giving the individual companies an equitable opportunity to market their sugar. In practice, marketing allotments are made whenever the supply of sugar available for marketing by an area seems likely to exceed the quota by a substantial amount.

A marketing allotment does not guarantee that a company can sell a given amount of sugar. It merely places a ceiling on the amount the company is permitted to sell in a year. Each company still has to compete with others, and competition in the sugar business is keen.

If a company markets more sugar than is permitted by an allotment, it is subject to a fine equal to three times the market value of the excess sugar marketed.

Proportionate Shares (Acreage Allotments)

The next step in implementing the sugar program is the setting of acreage allotments for the production of sugar beets and sugar cane. In the sugar program, the acreage allotments are known as proportionate shares. The purpose of acreage allotments is to regulate production of sugar beets and sugar cane so each domestic area will have enough sugar to fill its quota and to maintain a normal carryover, but not so much that burdensome excess supplies will be produced.

First a national sugar beet acreage figure is set. This is broken down to state figures, and the state share in turn is apportioned among individual farms. In working out the proportionate share for an individual farm, the Secretary considers the farm's history of growing the crop, and its ability to produce. Interests of small farmers, new producers, and tenants are considered.

Conditional Payments and the Excise Tax

Now we come to perhaps the most complicated parts of the sugar program — the conditional payments and the excise tax. These two things are tied together so closely they should be considered as one subject.

It has been pointed out that a sugar processing company is subject to a heavy penalty if it does not abide by restrictions imposed on it by the sugar program. The conditional payment and excise tax provisions of the law are the tools provided for enforcing compliance with the restrictions the program imposes upon the farmer. The payment and tax also help achieve a fair division of the sugar dollar among processor, farmer, and farm worker.

The case of an individual sugar beet farmer will illustrate how this part of the program operates.

The farmer considers the payment as part of the price he expects to receive for his sugar beets. He knows that to qualify for his conditional payment, he must fulfill certain restrictive requirements of the Sugar Act. He may market sugar beets from no more than his allotted acres. He must pay his field workers at least the minimum wages prescribed by the Secretary of Agriculture. He must not employ child labor.

The farmer knows that if he fails to observe any of these restrictions he will not receive his conditional payment and therefore he will not receive the full price he anticipated for his beet crop. This has proved to be a decidedly effective way of enforcing the restrictions imposed upon the farmer by the Sugar Act.

An excise tax of just over a half cent a pound on refined sugar — collected from beet sugar processors, cane sugar refiners, and importers of refined sugar — provides the United States Treasury with more than sufficient funds for making conditional payments. To show how the excise tax serves as part of the compliance machinery, the traditional sugar beet contract between grower and processor must be mentioned.

Since the late 1920's, several years before the Sugar Act was passed, the typical contract has provided for a sharing — between grower and processor — of the net return from the sale of sugar. The final return to the grower for his beets has depended upon the processor's net return from the sale of sugar. The Sugar Act has not disturbed this contractual arrangement, but of course in order to calculate the net return the tax must be deducted from the price the processor receives for sugar.

Thus, by means of the excise tax, the government collects part of the price of sugar which the farmer and processor would share under existing contracts if the tax did not exist. The government withholds the conditional payment until the farmer gives evidence that he has complied with all the conditions necessary to qualify for his payment.

Under the terms of existing contracts, both processor and grower, therefore, contribute in effect to the "payment fund." Payments are on a sliding scale, from 8/10 to 3/10 cent per pound of sugar produced from the farmer's crop. Larger payments per unit go to the smaller producer, and the larger producer may receive a payment actually smaller than his contribution through the tax. In order to qualify for his payment, the farmer must, among other things, pay at least prescribed minimum wages to his employees. Thus — in addition to its effect as an enforcement tool — the tax-conditional payment phase of the Sugar Act helps to achieve a distribution of the sugar dollar favorable to the family-size farm operator and to farm field workers.

Some Results of the United States Sugar Program

The sugar program has won high praise from many quarters. For example, as reported in the *Congressional Record* of July 19, 1956, Congressman Harold D. Cooley of North Carolina, said:

"The Sugar Act is one of the most successful of our farm programs, in terms of benefits to producers and dependable supplies at stabilized prices for consumers."

Mr. Cooley, chairman of the Agricultural Committee of the House of Representatives, pointed out that America consumes more than one-fifth of total world production of sugar, and that sugar consumption in this country continues to increase. He added:

"This is because the Sugar Act mantains a fair price to housewives, while giving a fair return to producers."

Certainly it is unique in that it has resulted in a sizable net gain to the United States Treasury. By 1958, collections of excise taxes under the program had exceeded conditional payments to growers and all costs of administering the program by more than $350,000,000.

The program has assured consumers of adequate supplies at reasonable prices. The uncertainties of supply that marked the sugar trade for many years have disappeared. One reason for this is the wide geographic dispersion of the several areas supplying the domestic market under the sugar program. This greatly minimizes the possibility that adverse weather conditions, or political, economic or military factors in any one area might result in a shortage of supplies for United States consumers.

Although prices under the program have not been rigid, the range of fluctuation has been much narrower than before. Average sugar prices have resisted upward pressures of prices and wages to a much greater degree than have average prices of all foods. For example, between 1934 and 1958, sugar prices rose one-fourth less than the average prices of all foods, and only one-third as much as per capita disposable income.

The sugar program permitted reduction of the tariff on Cuban sugar from 2 cents a pound in 1934 to $\frac{1}{2}$ cent a pound since 1948, and corresponding decreases (from $2\frac{1}{2}$ cents to $\frac{5}{8}$ cent) on sugar from other foreign countries. By guaranteeing a huge portion of our domestic sugar market for foreign producers, the program obviously has provided foreign purchasing power conducive to maintaining a large export trade.

The program's stabilizing effect on the domestic sugar industry has not lessened competition. This is evidenced by the steadily increasing efficiency of the sugar beet industry noted in earlier chapters. Good management and efficient operation still are prime requisites for success in the American sugar industry.

Chapter Nine

SUMMARY AND CONCLUSION

This, then, is the Beet Sugar Story. It is in reality the story of many things.

Of energy, for example. The energy of the sun, falling on the green leaf of a growing plant, sparks the remarkable process of nature which combines elements in the air and water to form sugar — which in turn provides energy for man. "Solar batteries" of nature — the broad, green leaves of the sugar beet plant — thus provide the beginning of the tale and yet in this beginning is a fascinating chronicle by itself.

Agriculture provides several more chapters of the saga. The deeply-rooted sugar beet plant fills a vital place in the farming pattern of twenty-two states. As a most dependable rotation crop, the sugar beet encourages sound farming and soil-maintaining practices in large areas of our country. The by-products — beet tops, pulp and molasses — are the means for feeding thousands of livestock which not only add to farm income and permit a well-rounded farming operation but also further enrich the soil.

The benefits of the sugar beet reach far beyond the farm. A reasonably sure crop, the beet gives a stability to farming which in turn spreads to businesses in scores of communities in the producing areas. Better business, schools, homes, churches, roads — these are some of the community assets traceable directly to the beet sugar industry. The decentralized nature of the industry — spread, as it is, from the Great Lakes to the Pacific Coast — brings these benefits to hundreds of thousands of people.

But quite aside from the economic importance of the industry, still another facet of this story, which could become a book in itself, is the importance of the industry to the very life of our nation.

Congress has repeatedly pointed out that for reasons of national defense a substantial supply of our sugar requirements should be produced in our own country. In reporting on amend-

73

BENEFITS OF INDUSTRY SPREAD

No other major crop produces so much revenue per acre for railroads (*above*) and other transportation businesses as does the sugar beet. Many men are kept on the job in quarries and mines obtaining the limerock, coal and coke (*below*) used in large quantities by beet sugar factories. Similarly, economic benefits of factories and sugar beet production spread to many other lines of business.

ments to sugar legislation in 1956, for example, committees of both the Senate and the House of Representatives made this statement:

"For many years it has been the policy of the United States government for defense and strategic reasons to preserve within the United States the ability to produce a portion of our sugar requirements. This has been done because sugar is an essential and vital food product needed by American consumers, the supply of which on a world-wide scale has been marked by periods of alternating scarcity and surplus."

Only the sugar produced in the United States is free from foreign influence and control. Although in the past foreign sugar-producing regions have been generally reliable, the situation could change at any time and there never can be assurance that it will not change. Also it is probable, because of the element of competition, that substantial domestic sugar production encourages reliability of supplies from foreign sugar areas.

Not only does this nation need a substantial domestic sugar industry, but for reasons of national security a substantial portion of that industry should be in the continental United States. Shipping is always at a premium during a war. The use of vessels to bring sugar to our shores reduces the number of ships available for importing other vital supplies and for transporting weapons and men to battlefields abroad. The sea-lanes are always open to attack, and with the development of atomic-powered submarines and atomic missiles it is possible that any future attacks on sources and shipments of sugar may be even more severe and disastrous than they have been during previous wars.

In the early part of World War II, when the submarine menace on the East Coast of the United States was at its height, it was impossible for a time to bring sugar from Puerto Rico or even across the narrow, 90-mile strait from Cuba to Florida. During a three-month period when this situation existed, 40 per cent of all the sugar consumed in the United States was beet sugar. It was regularly being distributed in eastern states far out of beet sugar's normal peacetime sales area. In fact, during a three-month period of 1943, 20 per cent of all the sugar distributed in New York state was beet sugar. Availability of beet sugar, produced in the continental United States, was vital during World War II; no one can predict how much more indispensable it may be in the future, in this atomic age.

Perhaps during peacetime we too often overlook the importance of beet sugar and of the industry that produces it. We are inclined to take sugar for granted.

It is inexpensive. The average American factory worker needs to be on his job only a few seconds more than three minutes to earn enough to buy a pound of sugar. In England, the average factory worker has to be on his job for ten minutes; in France, nineteen; in Italy, nearly thirty-eight; in Russia, 147 minutes or nearly two and one-half hours. Yes, sugar in America costs little — in money and in time — so we accept its availability as a matter of course.

We like sugar's pleasant flavor — by itself and in other foods. It tastes good. The good cook knows it improves the texture and enhances the appearance of other foods — as well as imparting an appealing taste. It is a food preservative. The dietitian recognizes all these things and knows also that it is a highly concentrated energy food; and more quickly than any other food it makes this energy available for human use — to move muscles, to walk, to run, to think.

And so the Beet Sugar Story is a story of many things — of agriculture, of community life, of scientific advancements, of national defense — of plant, man and machine — and above all, of a product that makes available for mankind the energy of the sun in a most pleasing and delightful form.

SUGAR BEET QUEEN

This lovely miss was chosen to reign over festivities held to celebrate the sugar beet harvest in one important producing area. Many communities annually hold celebrations to honor the sugar beet's importance to their local economies. By providing a dependable source of farm income, the sugar beet makes a steady market for hundreds of products of American industry and thus its beneficial effects are also felt far from the producing areas.

APPENDIX

TABLE 1. — BEET SUGAR FACTORIES IN UNITED STATES IN 1958 BY STATES

State	Number of Factories	Daily Capacity (Tons of Beets)
California	10	27,500
Colorado	15	29,400
Idaho	5	14,850
Iowa	1	1,800
Michigan	6	9,400
Minnesota	4	10,900
Montana	4	8,900
Nebraska	5	9,400
Ohio	3	3,550
Oregon	1	4,050
South Dakota	1	1,800
Utah	5	8,100
Washington	2	6,900
Wisconsin	1	1,100
Wyoming	3	5,700
Total	66	143,350

Source: United States Beet Sugar Association compilation.

TABLE 2. — SUGAR BEET ACREAGES HARVESTED, SUGAR BEET PRODUCTION, BEET SUGAR PRODUCTION IN UNITED STATES, ANNUALLY SINCE 1913.

	(1)	(2)	(3)	(4)	(5)	(6)
	Sugar Beets			Beet Sugar Production		
Crop Year[1]	Acreage Harvested 1,000 acres	Production 1,000 tons	Average Yield Per Acre Harvested tons	Tons Raw Value 1,000	100-lb. Bags Refined 1,000	Sugar Per Acre Harvested tons, raw value
1913	580	5,886	10.1	785	14,668	1.35
1914	483	5,585	11.6	773	14,441	1.60
1915	611	6,511	10.7	935	17,484	1.53
1916	665	6,228	9.4	878	16,413	1.32
1917	665	5,980	9.0	819	15,304	1.23
1918	594	5,949	10.0	814	15,219	1.37
1919	692	6,421	9.3	777	14,529	1.12
1920	872	8,538	9.8	1,165	21,780	1.34
1921	815	7,782	9.5	1,091	20,400	1.34
1922	530	5,183	9.8	722	13,500	1.36
1923	657	7,006	10.7	943	17,620	1.43
1924	816	7,508	9.2	1,166	21,800	1.43
1925	648	7,381	11.4	977	18,260	1.51
1926	677	7,223	10.7	960	17,940	1.42
1927	721	7,753	10.8	1,170	21,860	1.62
1928	644	7,101	11.0	1,135	21,220	1.76
1929	688	7,315	10.6	1,089	20,360	1.58
1930	776	9,199	11.9	1,293	24,160	1.66
1931	713	7,903	11.1	1,237	23,120	1.73
1932	764	9,070	11.9	1,452	27,140	1.90
1933	983	11,030	11.2	1,757	32,840	1.79
1934	770	7,519	9.8	1,241	23,200	1.61
1935	763	7,908	10.4	1,268	23,700	1.66
1936	776	9,029	11.6	1,395	26,080	1.79
1937	755	8,772	11.6	1,375	25,701	1.82
1938	931	11,579	12.4	1,802	33,688	1.93

(Continued on next page)

TABLE 2. (Continued) — SUGAR BEET ACREAGES HARVESTED, SUGAR BEET PRODUCTION, BEET SUGAR PRODUCTION IN UNITED STATES, ANNUALLY SINCE 1913.

	(1) Sugar Beets	(2)	(3)	(4) Beet Sugar Production	(5)	(6)
Crop Year[1]	Acreage Harvested 1,000 acres	Production 1,000 tons	Average Yield Per Acre Harvested tons	Tons Raw Value 1,000	100-lb. Bags Refined 1,000	Sugar Per Acre Harvested tons, raw value
1939	916	10,770	11.8	1,760	32,896	1.92
1940	914	12,291	13.5	1,894	35,404	2.07
1941	753	10,298	13.7	1,584	29,608	2.10
1942	953	11,672	12.2	1,725	32,237	1.81
1943	545	6,523	12.0	998	18,651	1.83
1944	556	6,757	12.1	1,056	19,730	1.90
1945	715	8,673	12.1	1,280	23,918	1.79
1946	818	10,863	13.3	1,569	29,318	1.91
1947	893	12,684	14.2	1,867	34,902	2.10
1948	670	9,073	13.5	1,312	24,530	1.96
1949	703	10,468	14.9	1,608	30,057	2.29
1950	924	13,585	14.7	2,015	37,661	2.18
1951	696	10,497	15.1	1,541	28,804	2.21
1952	661	10,181	15.4	1,519	28,386	2.30
1953	765	12,507	16.3	1,873	35,005	2.45
1954	855	13,766	16.1	1,998	37,349	2.33
1955	744	12,238	16.5	1,730	32,339	2.32
1956	789	13,107	16.6	1,971	36,850	2.50
1957	882	15,645	17.7	2,216	41,418	2.51

SOURCES: Cols. 1, 2, 3 — Sugar Statistics — Vol. II (Dec. 1954 and supplements), Table 7, p. 7. United States Department of Agriculture.

Col. 4 — Ibid., Table 2, p. 2.
Col. 5 — Ibid., Table 1, p. 1.
Col. 6 — Calculated from Columns 1 and 4.

[1] — Crop year based upon calendar year in which crop was planted.

TABLE 3. — SUGAR BEETS: ACREAGE PLANTED AND HARVESTED, YIELD PER ACRE AND PRODUCTION BY STATES

State	Acreage Planted					Acreage Harvested				
	Average 1944-53 (Thousand Acres)	1954	1955	1956	1957	Average 1944-53 (Thousand Acres)	1954	1955	1956	1957
Calif.*	151	225	168	179	202	141	218	163	171	196
Colo.	142	151	123	131	140	131	115	102	121	136
Idaho	79	93	80	81	91	70	89	77	75	88
Kans.	7	7	7	7	9	6	6	6	7	9
Mich.	81	77	64	70	74	68	64	60	63	70
Minn.	49	76	66	67	75	45	73	64	65	66
Mont.	65	56	51	52	58	60	54	50	51	57
Nebr.	59	68	56	59	62	54	60	46	56	60
N. Dak.	24	38	35	35	39	22	37	34	35	37
Ohio	22	18	19	19	23	18	15	18	16	22
Oreg.	20	19	18	18	19	18	18	17	17	19
S. Dak.	5	7	5	6	5	5	6	5	5	5
Utah	35	36	30	28	31	32	33	29	27	29
Wash.	19	36	31	31	34	18	34	28	30	34
Wis.	13	14	6	7	8	11	11	6	6	8
Wyo.	35	40	34	35	38	32	36	30	34	37
Other States	7	6	5	6	6	6	5	5	5	6
U.S.	814	964	798	831	916	736	876	740	784	878

State	Yield Per Harvested Acre					Production				
	Average 1944-53 (Tons)	1954	1955	1956	1957	Average 1944-53 (Thousand Tons)	1954	1955	1956	1957
Calif.*	18.0	21.2	20.7	20.5	22.0	2.554	4,632	3,365	3.500	4.308
Colo.	14.6	14.4	15.9	15.7	17.7	1,897	1,654	1,621	1,893	2,399
Idaho	17.1	17.6	18.7	20.7	20.2	1,201	1,569	1,433	1.549	1,777
Kans.	9.7	10.2	14.8	14.9	15.7	57	62	96	106	140
Mich.	9.5	12.0	14.7	11.0	13.0	633	771	885	696	907
Minn.	10.0	11.2	12.0	12.0	12.7	447	819	771	772	840
Mont.	12.0	12.6	14.5	14.8	15.7	709	683	724	754	891
Nebr.	13.0	13.1	14.4	15.1	15.0	699	786	665	848	895
N. Dak.	10.2	11.3	11.7	11.4	12.9	223	418	398	397	477
Ohio	10.4	16.2	15.5	12.2	13.2	183	247	279	199	289
Oreg.	19.5	21.7	22.7	24.7	24.1	346	389	381	428	462
S. Dak.	10.4	12.5	12.5	13.0	12.6	49	75	64	65	63
Utah	14.4	16.2	15.1	17.2	16.2	467	535	437	462	470
Wash.	20.8	22.3	20.0	23.2	24.7	375	761	553	707	846
Wis.	9.8	12.2	9.3	10.2	9.9	108	135	57	65	78
Wyo.	12.6	13.1	13.9	14.0	15.1	411	475	421	472	559
Other States	11.8	14.8	16.2	15.1	16.3	73	71	78	80	96
U.S.	14.1	16.1	16.5	16.6	17.7	10,431	14,082	12,228	12,993	15,497

*Relates to year of harvest, including acreage planted in preceding fall.

Source: Compiled by United States Beet Sugar Association from United States Department of Agriculture reports.

TABLE 4. — BEET SUGAR: PRODUCTION BY STATES, CROP YEARS SINCE 1935-36

(100-lb. bags, refined)

State	1935-36	1936-37	1937-38	1938-39	1939-40	1940-41	1941-42
California	4,776,092	6,201,616	5,758,873	6,741,870	9,060,265	9,317,154	6,202,267
Colorado	5,897,018	6,695,153	6,053,669	6,103,411	5,348,464	6,248,656	5,941,389
Idaho	1,439,248	1,827,581	2,000,559	2,855,520	2,547,049	2,904,616	2,133,081
Indiana	222,000	211,901	186,762	301,251	274,517	301,661	275,567
Iowa	290,152	257,594	254,251	432,172	370,038	428,138	288,891
Kansas	109,406	157,602	152,777	223,468	142,755	273,693	205,677
Michigan	1,949,895	2,328,597	1,581,944	3,427,364	3,237,790	3,348,989	3,167,357
Minnesota	666,747	462,082	739,942	913,617	680,970	891,274	692,238
Montana	1,675,256	1,827,505	2,431,080	2,837,370	2,800,599	3,269,444	2,356,848
Nebraska	1,908,225	2,107,298	2,258,368	2,705,911	2,114,782	2,302,958	2,417,620
Ohio	647,778	555,795	273,057	862,201	834,380	899,141	919,865
Oregon	—	—	—	698,570	719,840	748,000	699,360
South Dakota	338,549	125,273	134,794	307,316	177,357	246,671	220,062
Utah	1,527,893	1,398,642	1,622,324	2,212,149	2,011,772	1,476,622	1,635,269
Washington	96,178	108,046	286,366	571,981	642,828	645,170	630,120
Wisconsin	181,435	162,493	153,894	320,262	176,540	238,685	201,455
Wyoming	1,852,807	1,673,215	1,874,786	2,121,122	1,837,702	1,863,335	1,576,603
Total Bags	23,578,679	26,100,393	25,764,446	33,635,555	32,977,648	35,404,207	29,563,669
Total—(Short Tons, Raw Value)	1,261,459	1,396,371	1,378,398	1,799,502	1,764,304	1,894,125	1,581,656

(Continued on next page)

TABLE 4. (Continued) — BEET SUGAR: PRODUCTION BY STATES, CROP YEARS SINCE 1935-36

(100-lb. bags, refined)

State	1942-43	1943-44	1944-45	1945-46	1946-47	1947-48	1948-49
California	6,945,969	3,253,580	3,567,092	4,629,046	6,754,709	8,731,128	6,637,041
Colorado	6,457,614	4,966,810	4,597,131	5,459,351	5,375,262	7,575,511	4,121,133
Idaho	2,896,789	1,478,248	1,607,743	2,106,323	2,877,415	4,567,566	2,926,877
Indiana	355,181	62,721	—	—	—	—	—
Iowa	348,441	215,845	259,895	322,133	440,563	286,660	292,565
Kansas	180,041	101,033	128,350	144,176	168,295	241,735	105,972
Michigan	3,448,951	998,312	1,620,368	1,921,770	2,883,715	1,221,111	1,541,754
Minnesota	890,232	584,810	791,727	792,918	1,019,480	720,117	1,175,074
Montana	2,825,771	2,071,715	2,176,019	2,488,852	2,343,981	2,524,421	1,886,520
Nebraska	2,074,723	1,471,483	1,353,739	1,468,886	1,864,646	2,069,013	1,114,959
Ohio	1,082,767	211,427	333,635	565,787	611,151	329,256	358,153
Oregon	837,140	692,610	677,840	903,838	1,184,442	1,644,437	1,495,701
South Dakota	183,642	110,483	112,366	160,311	191,577	146,449	89,766
Utah	1,634,659	1,291,563	1,098,001	1,123,906	1,396,608	2,109,443	1,165,486
Washington	739,317	585,216	480,902	686,849	830,791	984,393	715,800
Wisconsin	155,716	113,292	139,611	169,809	164,166	368,213	154,822
Wyoming	1,236,561	557,038	792,399	975,838	1,158,902	1,324,408	765,672
Total Bags	32,293,514	18,766,186	19,736,818	23,919,793	29,265,703	34,843,861	24,547,295
Total—(Short Tons, Raw Value)	1,727,703	1,003,991	1,055,920	1,279,709	1,565,715	1,864,146	1,313,280

(Continued on next page)

TABLE 4. (Continued) — BEET SUGAR: PRODUCTION BY STATES, CROP YEARS SINCE 1935-36

(100-lb. bags, refined)

State	1949-50	1950-51	1951-52	1952-53	1953-54	1954-55	1955-56	1956-57	1957-58
California	8,239,866	10,716,559	7,259,193	7,554,664	10,194,165	12,067,847	9,050,179	9,431,015	11,240,300
Colorado	6,218,877	7,464,951	6,060,519	6,005,965	6,370,942	5,071,744	4,968,020	6,525,555	7,836,142
Idaho	2,509,882	3,638,938	2,892,297	2,502,624	3,675,051	3,952,099	3,293,208	3,769,041	4,408,812
Indiana									—
Iowa	427,828	389,516	467,570	344,186	355,323	238,320	141,683	297,350	231,371
Kansas	110,349	135,125	74,640	115,001	65,013	141,614	204,978	—	—
Michigan	2,338,176	2,909,407	1,561,181	1,461,992	1,527,124	1,528,072	1,996,229	1,797,857	1,972,172
Minnesota	1,450,679	1,378,000	1,828,709	1,716,377	2,028,638	2,701,568	2,550,577	2,781,638	2,667,926
Montana	2,050,336	2,272,283	1,569,316	1,495,709	1,806,025	2,038,666	2,241,587	2,477,915	2,577,635
Nebraska	1,486,305	2,179,070	1,720,570	1,957,116	2,098,999	1,836,199	1,596,911	2,365,930	2,364,582
Ohio	570,340	575,622	369,802	359,971	511,951	681,227	616,807	564,923	758,929
Oregon	1,299,345	1,519,529	1,276,790	1,270,888	1,453,938	1,674,157	1,392,174	1,535,735	1,647,755
South Dakota	153,552	211,636	180,536	232,712	191,943	268,981	232,352	301,613	245,077
Utah	1,245,404	1,518,910	1,111,240	717,104	1,201,772	1,529,621	1,198,178	1,382,209	1,364,153
Washington	850,224	1,184,345	1,144,514	1,324,334	1,937,714	2,042,518	1,483,805	1,914,240	2,247,664
Wisconsin	236,157	402,336	139,120	170,174	212,111	245,241	205,108	233,375	245,858
Wyoming	1,040,775	1,213,618	1,168,418	1,189,383	1,387,107	1,341,025	1,149,694	1,477,339	1,551,413
Total Bags	30,228,095	37,709,845	28,824,415	28,418,200	35,017,816	37,358,899	32,321,490	36,855,735	41,359,789
Total—(Short Tons, Raw Value)	1,617,203	2,017,477	1,542,106	1,520,374	1,873,453	1,998,701	1,729,200	1,971,782	2,212,748

Source: Compiled by United States Beet Sugar Association.

CHART A — WHOLESALE SUGAR PRICES AND PER CAPITA DISPOSABLE INCOME IN THE UNITED STATES, 1910-1958

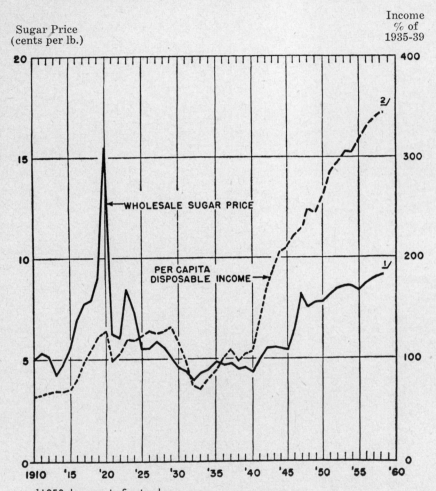

Sugar Price
(cents per lb.)

Income
% of
1935-39

¹1958 January to September.
²Annual rate for second quarter 1958.

Source: *Sugar Reports* 78 (Oct., 1958), Figure 6, p. 20. United States Department of Agriculture.

CHART B — REFINED SUGAR PRICES, AND INDEX OF ALL FOOD PRICES,
AT WHOLESALE IN THE UNITED STATES, 1860-1958

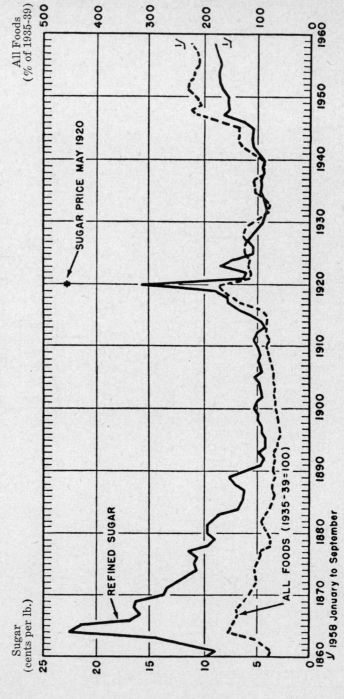

Source: *Sugar Reports* 78 (Oct., 1958), Figure 7, p. 22. United States Department of Agriculture.

FOR ADDITIONAL READING

General

Cottrell, R. H. (ed.). *Beet Sugar Economics.* Caldwell, Idaho: The Caxton Printers, Ltd., 1952. 379 pp. (A comprehensive book on the industry, with emphasis on economics of sugar beet production and processing.)

McGinnis, R. A. (ed.). *Beet-Sugar Technology.* New York: Reinhold Publishing Corporation, 1951. 574 pp. (Another comprehensive book, with particular emphasis on technology of growing and processing sugar beets.)

Maynard, E. J. *Beets & Meat.* Denver: Through the Leaves Press, 1950. 102 pp. (A practical manual for fattening cattle and sheep with sugar beet by-products.)

Sugar Information, Inc. *Sugar.* New York: Sugar Information, Inc., c. 1950. 36 pp. (An illustrated story of the production and processing of sugar.)

——————. *Sugar — Its Types and Uses.* New York: Sugar Information, Inc., 1954 (third edition). 32 pp. (Authoritative discussion of sugar and competitive products; of special interest to industrial users of sugar.)

——————. *Sugar as a Food.* New York: Sugar Information, Inc., 1955. 32 pp. (Documented report on research studies involving food, nutrition, diet and health, and their relation to sugar.)

Sugar Research Foundation, Inc. *The Sugar Molecule.* New York: Sugar Research Foundation, Inc. Periodical. (Contains timely articles by authorities on sugar and its uses.)

Taylor, Fred G. *A Saga of Sugar.* Salt Lake City: Utah-Idaho Sugar Company, Deseret News Press, 1944. 234 pp. (Well-told and well-documented story of the beet sugar industry in the Rocky Mountain West, with emphasis on the dramatic endeavors of the Mormons in Utah.)

United States Beet Sugar Association. *American Beet Sugar Companies, 1957-1958.* Washington, D.C.: United States Beet Sugar Association, 1958. 16 pp. (Directory of beet sugar companies in the United States and Canada; published annually.)

United States Department of Agriculture. *The United States Sugar Program. Agricultural Information Bulletin No. 111.* Washington, D.C.: United States Government Printing Office, 1953. 34 pp. (Describes background and operations of the Sugar Act, with particular reference to the Sugar Act of 1948, as amended in 1951.)

Western Beet Sugar Producers, Inc. *The United States Beet Sugar Industry.* San Francisco: Western Beet Sugar Producers, Inc., 1956. 16 pp. (Pamphlet describing briefly the history of the industry and its place in the American economy.)

Technical

American Society of Sugar Beet Technologists. *Journal.* Fort Collins, Colo.: The American Society of Sugar Beet Technologists. Published quarterly. (Technical papers on wide variety of subjects concerning all phases of sugar beet plant breeding, growing, and processing.)

——————. *Proceedings.* Fort Collins, Colo.: The American Society of Sugar Beet Technologists. Published biennially from 1940 through 1954. Has been succeeded by the *Journal,* above. (Technical papers presented at the biennial meetings of the Society.)

Statistical

United States Department of Agriculture. *Sugar Statistics.* 2 vols. Washington, D.C.: United States Government Printing Office, Vol. I 1957 (rev.), Vol. II 1954. (Statistics on sugar deliveries from areas marketing in the United States, and production and related statistics on domestic producing areas.)

——————. *Sugar Reports.* Issued monthly. Washington, D.C.: Sugar Division, Commodity Stabilization Service, United States Department of Agriculture. (Current sugar production and distribution statistics.)

Children's Books

Allee, Veva Elwell, and Fogata, Robert. *From Sugar Beets to Beet Sugar.* Los Angeles: Melmont Publishers, Inc., 1956. 24 pp. (A simple, step-by-step explanation of the sugar-extracting process, illustrated with full-page photographs. For younger children.)

Burt, Olive W. *Peter's Sugar Farm*. New York: Henry Holt and Company, Inc., 1954. 90 pp. (A delightful story of a boy who learns about sugar beets when his family moves to a farm. For children 9 to 12 years of age.)

For Teachers

United States Beet Sugar Association. *The Sugar Beet Goes to School*. Washington, D.C.: United States Beet Sugar Association, 1951. 16 pp. Manual plus student work sheets and four large wall charts. (A teaching kit designed as an interesting and effective unit of work for intermediate and upper grades. Can be used alone or with *The Beet Sugar Story* as a reference.)

Western Beet Sugar Producers, Inc. *Let's Talk about Sugar*. San Francisco: Western Beet Sugar Producers, Inc., 1955 (rev.). (A manual for home economics instructors. Presents important facts about sugar, its role in nutrition and in cookery. Includes taste testing and product judging procedure and sample score sheet. Can be used alone or with student leaflet, *Know Your Way with Sugar*. See below.)

—————. *Know Your Way with Sugar*. San Francisco: Western Beet Sugar Producers, Inc., 1956 (rev.). 4 pp. (Classroom leaflet for students of home economics. Contains information and recipes for use of sugar in a variety of foods, including cakes, cookies, candy, quick breads, jellies, etc., and the use of sugar in canning and freezing.)

Recipes

Beet sugar may be used in all recipes that call for sugar. Western Beet Sugar Producers, Inc., 461 Market Street, San Francisco 5, California, has prepared an interesting series of recipe booklets available without charge, including the following titles: *Answers by the Canning Doctor, Candy and How, Fashions in Frostings, Just Desserts, The Way of All Cookies, Well Preserved, Sauce-y Toppings, Simple Desserts Made Fancy, Elegant Meringue, Springtime Pies*.

Company Publications

Several of the beet sugar companies publish periodicals for sugar beet growers and also issue other publications. A list of such material may be obtained from the United States Beet Sugar Association, 920 Tower Building, Washington, D.C., or from Western Beet Sugar Producers, Inc., 461 Market Street, San Francisco 5, California.

Motion Pictures

Motion pictures on the beet sugar industry are available for use in classrooms and for showing to other groups. Further information is available from Western Beet Sugar Producers, Inc., 461 Market Street, San Francisco 5, California.

Libraries

Several libraries in the United States have outstanding collections of books and other material on sugar beets and beet sugar. Among such libraries are the following:

Franklin Institute Library Philadelphia, Pennsylvania	University of California College of Agriculture Davis, California
Colorado State University Fort Collins, Colorado	Library of Congress Washington, D.C.
University of California Berkeley, California	United States Department of Agriculture Washington, D.C.